The

NORTON MIX

NORTON
CUSTOM

W · W · NORTON & COMPANY · *New York* · *London*

The
NORTON MIX

A CUSTOM PUBLICATION

Readings on Science

and Technology

W. W. Norton & Company has been independent since its founding in 1923, when William Warder Norton and Mary D. Herter Norton first published lectures delivered at the People's Institute, the adult education division of New York City's Cooper Union. The firm soon expanded its program beyond the Institute, publishing books by celebrated academics from America and abroad. By mid-century, the two major pillars of Norton's publishing program— trade books and college texts—were firmly established. In the 1950s, the Norton family transferred control of the company to its employees, and today—with a staff of four hundred and a comparable number of trade, college, and professional titles published each year— W. W. Norton & Company stands as the largest and oldest publishing house owned wholly by its employees.

Copyright © 2011 by W. W. Norton & Company, Inc.

Editor: Katie Hannah
Developmental editors: Mike Fleming and Erin Granville
Managing editor: Marian Johnson
Project editor: Melissa Atkin
Editorial assistant: Sophie Hagen
Production managers: Eric Pier-Hocking and Ashley Horna
Permissions editor: Nancy Rodwan
Photo permissions editor: Trish Marx
Designer: Toni Krass
Cover designs: Debra Morton-Hoyt
Emedia editor: Eileen Connell
Marketing manager: Scott Berzon
Proofreaders: Paulette McGee, Ben Reynolds
Composition: RR Donnelley
Manufacturing: RR Donnelley

ISBN-13 978-0-393-15745-1

W. W. Norton & Company, Inc., 500 Fifth Avenue, New York, N.Y. 10110
www.wwnorton.com
W. W. Norton & Company Ltd., Castle House, 75/76 Wells Street, London W1T 3QT

GENERAL EDITORS

ELIZABETH RODRIGUEZ KESSLER
COORDINATING EDITOR
University of Houston

JEFFREY ANDELORA
Mesa Community College

KATHARINE N. INGS
Manchester College

ANGELA L. JONES
Western Kentucky University

CHRISTOPHER KELLER
University of Texas–Pan American

WITH CONTRIBUTIONS FROM
CEDRIC BURROWS
University of Kansas

LORI CHASTAINE
Boise State University

MICHELLE L. CHESTER
Towson University

WANDA FRIES
Somerset Community College

HOLLY HASSEL
University of Wisconsin–Marathon County

BETH DINATALE JOHNSON
Ursuline College

Contents

Contents

DIANE ACKERMAN { *Why Leaves Turn Color in the Fall*

DIANE ACKERMAN (b. 1948) is a writer who earned her MA, MFA, and PhD at Cornell University. Ackerman has written more than twenty books—nonfiction and poetry for adults as well as nature books for children—that have received numerous awards. Ackerman has also published essays about nature and human nature in the *New York Times*, *Smithsonian*, *Parade*, *The New Yorker*, and *National Geographic*, among other publications. *A Natural History of the Senses*, her acclaimed 1990 volume of essays, inspired the series *Mystery of the Senses* on PBS television, which Ackerman hosted.

This selection from *A Natural History of the Senses* explains the natural processes that cause leaves to change color in the fall. Much of Ackerman's work, including this essay, demonstrates her ability to convey scientific information in a way that is both engaging and relevant for non-scientists. Notice the ideas from different fields of study that Ackerman draws together here as she explains the seasonal cycle of leaves.

THE STEALTH OF AUTUMN CATCHES one unaware. Was that a goldfinch perching in the early September woods, or just the first turning leaf? A red-winged blackbird or a sugar maple closing up shop for the winter? Keen-eyed as leopards, we stand still and squint hard, looking for signs of movement. Early-morning frost sits heavily on the grass, and turns barbed wire into a string of stars. On a distant hill, a small square of yellow appears to be a lighted stage. At last the truth dawns on us: Fall is staggering in, right on schedule, with its baggage of chilly nights, macabre holidays, and spectacular, heart-stoppingly beautiful leaves. Soon the leaves will start cringing on the trees, and roll up in clenched fists before they actually fall off. Dry seedpods will rattle like tiny gourds. But first there will be weeks of gushing color so bright, so pastel, so confettilike, that people will travel up and down the East Coast just to stare at it—a whole season of leaves.

Where do the colors come from? Sunlight rules most living things with its golden edicts. When the days begin to shorten, soon after the summer solstice on June 21, a tree reconsiders its leaves. All summer it feeds them so they can process sunlight, but in the dog days of summer the tree begins pulling nutrients back into its trunk and roots, pares down, and gradually chokes off its leaves. A corky layer of cells forms at the leaves' slender petioles, then scars over. Undernourished, the leaves stop producing the pigment chlorophyll, and photosynthesis ceases. Animals can migrate, hibernate, or store food to prepare for winter. But where can a tree go? It survives by dropping its leaves, and by the end of autumn only a few fragile threads of fluid-carrying xylem hold leaves to their stems.

A turning leaf stays partly green at first, then reveals splotches of yellow and red as the chlorophyll gradually breaks down. Dark green seems to stay longest in the veins, outlining and defining them. During the summer, chlorophyll dissolves in the heat and light, but it is also being steadily replaced. In the fall, on the other hand, no new pigment is produced, and so we notice the other colors that were always there, right in the leaf, although chlorophyll's shocking green hid them from view. With their camouflage gone, we see these colors for the first time all year, and marvel, but they were always there, hidden like a vivid secret beneath the hot glowing greens of summer.

The most spectacular range of fall foliage occurs in the northeastern United States and in eastern China, where the leaves are robustly colored, thanks in part to a rich climate. European maples don't achieve the same flaming reds as their American relatives, which thrive on cold nights and sunny days. In Europe, the warm, humid weather turns the leaves brown or mildly yellow. Anthocyanin, the pigment that gives apples their red and turns leaves red or red-violet, is produced by sugars that remain in the leaf after the supply of nutrients dwindles. Unlike the carotenoids, which color carrots, squash, and corn, and turn leaves orange and yellow, anthocyanin varies from year to year, depending on the temperature and amount of sunlight. The fiercest colors occur in years when the fall sunlight is strongest and the nights are cool and dry (a state of grace scientists find vexing to forecast). This is also why leaves appear dizzyingly bright and clear on a sunny fall day: The anthocyanin flashes like a marquee.

Not all leaves turn the same colors. Elms, weeping willows, and the ancient ginkgo all grow radiant yellow, along with hickories, aspens, bottlebrush buckeyes, cottonwoods, and tall, keening poplars. Basswood turns bronze, birches bright gold. Water-loving maples put on a symphonic display of scarlets. Sumacs turn red, too, as do flowering dogwoods, black gums, and sweet gums. Though some oaks yellow, most turn a pinkish brown. The farmlands also change color, as tepees of cornstalks and bales of shredded-wheat-textured hay stand drying in the fields. In some spots, one slope of a hill may be green and the other already in bright color, because the hillside facing south gets more sun and heat than the northern one.

An odd feature of the colors is that they don't seem to have any special purpose. We are predisposed to respond to their beauty, of course. They shimmer with the colors of sunset, spring flowers, the tawny buff of a colt's pretty rump, the shuddering pink of a blush. Animals and flowers color for a reason—adaptation to their environment—but there is no adaptive reason for leaves to color so beautifully in the fall any more than there is for the sky or ocean to be blue. It's just one of the haphazard marvels the planet bestows every year. We find the sizzling colors thrilling, and in a sense they dupe us. Colored like living things, they signal death and disintegration. In time, they will become fragile and, like the body, return to dust. They are as we hope our own fate will be when we die: Not to vanish, just to sublime from one beautiful state into another. Though leaves lose their green life, they bloom with urgent colors, as the woods grow mummified day by day, and Nature becomes more carnal, mute, and radiant.

We call the season "fall," from the Old English *feallan*, to fall, which leads back through time to the Indo-European *phol*, which also means to fall. So the word and the idea are both extremely ancient, and

3

haven't really changed since the first of our kind needed a name for fall's leafy abundance. As we say the word, we're reminded of that other Fall, in the garden of Eden, when fig leaves never withered and scales fell from our eyes. Fall is the time when leaves fall from the trees, just as spring is when flowers spring up, summer is when we simmer, and winter is when we whine from the cold.

Children love to play in piles of leaves, hurling them into the air like confetti, leaping into soft unruly mattresses of them. For children, leaf fall is just one of the odder figments of Nature, like hailstones or snowflakes. Walk down a lane overhung with trees in the never-never land of autumn, and you will forget about time and death, lost in the sheer delicious spill of color. Adam and Eve concealed their nakedness with leaves, remember? Leaves have always hidden our awkward secrets.

But how do the colored leaves fall? As a leaf ages, the growth hormone, auxin, fades, and cells at the base of the petiole divide. Two or three rows of small cells, lying at right angles to the axis of the petiole, react with water, then come apart, leaving the petioles hanging on by only a few threads of xylem. A light breeze, and the leaves are airborne. They glide and swoop, rocking in invisible cradles. They are all wing and may flutter from yard to yard on small whirlwinds or updrafts, swiveling as they go. Firmly tethered to earth, we love to see things rise up and fly—soap bubbles, balloons, birds, fall leaves. They remind us that the end of a season is capricious, as is the end of life. We especially like the way leaves rock, careen, and swoop as they fall. Everyone knows the motion. Pilots sometimes do a maneuver called a "falling leaf," in which the plane loses altitude quickly and on purpose, by slipping first to the right, then to the left. The machine weighs a ton or more, but in one pilot's mind it is a weightless thing, a falling leaf. She has seen the motion before, in the Vermont woods where she played as a child. Below her the trees radiate gold, copper, and red. Leaves are falling, although she can't see them fall, as she falls, swooping down for a closer view.

At last the leaves leave. But first they turn color and thrill us for weeks on end. Then they crunch and crackle underfoot. They *shush*, as children drag their small feet through leaves heaped along the curb. Dark, slimy mats of leaves cling to one's heels after a rain. A damp, stuccolike mortar of semidecayed leaves protects the tender shoots with a roof until spring, and makes a rich humus. An occasional bulge or ripple in the leafy mounds signals a shrew or a field mouse tunneling out of sight. Sometimes one finds in fossil stones the imprint of a leaf, long since disintegrated, whose outlines remind us how detailed, vibrant, and alive are the things of this earth that perish.

STUDY QUESTIONS

1. Is the seasonal change of leaves equally dramatic in all areas of the world? Why or why not?

2. Ackerman uses many literary techniques in this selection. Select one of those techniques (e.g., IMAGERY, descriptive language, third-person plural POINT OF VIEW), give an example of it, and explain how it influences your reading of the piece.

3. *For Writing.* In paragraph 6, Ackerman notes that "there is no adaptive reason for leaves to color so beautifully in the fall," and she calls this change "one of the haphazard marvels the planet bestows every year." What is a natural "marvel" in your hometown or college area? What makes you identify it as a "marvel"? In an essay, describe this "marvel" using concrete language and explain what makes it worth noting or studying.

RUSSELL BAKER { *The Plot Against People*

RUSSELL BAKER (b. 1925), journalist, columnist, and essayist, was born in
Morrisonville, Virginia, and earned a BA from the Johns Hopkins University
in 1947. From 1962 to 2008 he wrote the nationally syndicated "Observer"
column for the *New York Times*, for which he won a Pulitzer Prize in 1979.
He received a second Pulitzer in 1983 for his autobiography *Growing Up*.
His other books include *The Good Times* (1992), a continuation of *Growing
Up*, and several collections of his columns and essays. Baker hosted PBS's
Masterpiece Theatre from 1992 to 2004.

In "The Plot against People," Baker humorously employs science to make
sense out of decidedly unscientific occurrences: everyday objects getting
broken or lost. As he classifies each type of object in its proper scientific category, Baker proposes a theory to explain why inanimate objects are in such
adversarial relationships with their owners. Note how he carefully builds his
case through logical reasoning and personification.

INANIMATE OBJECTS ARE CLASSIFIED SCIENTIFICALLY into three
major categories—those that don't work, those that break down and
those that get lost.

The goal of all inanimate objects is to resist man and ultimately to
defeat him, and the three major classifications are based on the method
each object uses to achieve its purpose. As a general rule, any object capable of breaking down at the moment when it is most needed will do
so. The automobile is typical of the category.

With the cunning typical of its breed, the automobile never breaks
down while entering a filling station with a large staff of idle mechan-

ics. It waits until it reaches a downtown intersection in the middle of the rush hour, or until it is fully loaded with family and luggage on the Ohio Turnpike.

Thus it creates maximum misery, inconvenience, frustration and irritability among its human cargo, thereby reducing its owner's life span.

Washing machines, garbage disposals, lawn mowers, light bulbs, 5 automatic laundry dryers, water pipes, furnaces, electrical fuses, television tubes, hose nozzles, tape recorders, slide projectors—all are in league with the automobile to take their turn at breaking down whenever life threatens to flow smoothly for their human enemies.

Many inanimate objects, of course, find it extremely difficult to break down. Pliers, for example, and gloves and keys are almost totally incapable of breaking down. Therefore, they have had to evolve a different technique for resisting man.

A PLAUSIBLE THEORY

They get lost. Science has still not solved the mystery of how they do it, and no man has ever caught one of them in the act of getting lost. The most plausible theory is that they have developed a secret method of locomotion which they are able to conceal the instant a human eye falls upon them.

It is not uncommon for a pair of pliers to climb all the way from the cellar to the attic in its single-minded determination to raise its owner's blood pressure. Keys have been known to burrow three feet under mattresses. Women's purses, despite their great weight, frequently travel through six or seven rooms to find hiding space under a couch.

Scientists have been struck by the fact that things that break down virtually never get lost, while things that get lost hardly ever break down.

A furnace, for example, will invariably break down at the depth of 10 the first winter cold wave, but it will never get lost. A woman's purse, which after all does have some inherent capacity for breaking down, hardly ever does; it almost invariably chooses to get lost.

Some persons believe this constitutes evidence that inanimate objects are not entirely hostile to man, and that a negotiated peace is possible. After all, they point out, a furnace could infuriate a man even more thoroughly by getting lost than by breaking down, just as a glove could upset him far more by breaking down than by getting lost.

Not everyone agrees, however, that this indicates a conciliatory attitude among inanimate objects. Many say it merely proves that furnaces, gloves and pliers are incredibly stupid.

The third class of objects—those that don't work—is the most curious of all. These include such objects as barometers, car clocks, cigarette lighters, flashlights and toy-train locomotives. It is inaccurate, of course, to say that they never work. They work once, usually for the first few hours after being brought home, and then quit. Thereafter, they never work again.

In fact, it is widely assumed that they are built for the purpose of not working. Some people have reached advanced ages without ever seeing some of these objects—barometers, for example—in working order.

Science is utterly baffled by the entire category. There are many theories about it. The most interesting holds that the things that don't work have attained the highest state possible for an inanimate object, the state to which things that break down and things that get lost can still only aspire.

THEY GIVE PEACE

They have truly defeated man by conditioning him never to expect anything of them, and in return they have given man the only peace he receives from inanimate society. He does not expect his barometer to work, his electric locomotive to run, his cigarette lighter to light or his flashlight to illuminate, and when they don't, it does not raise his blood pressure.

He cannot attain that peace with furnaces and keys and cars and women's purses as long as he demands that they work for their keep.

9

STUDY QUESTIONS

1. What are the three major categories that Baker establishes in his essay, and what inanimate objects does he mention as representative examples of each?

2. How does Baker use science, humor, and personification as he presents his CLASSIFICATION scheme? What is the effect of classifying the adversarial relationship between inanimate objects and humans from a scientific perspective?

3. *For Writing.* Update this opinion piece (written in 1968) for your generation. Create several categories and, in an essay, classify the relationships you have with several items you own—such as an iPod, a cell phone, or a laptop computer.

DAVE BARRY $\left\{\begin{array}{l}\textit{A GPS Helps a Guy Always}\\\textit{Know Where His Couch Is}\end{array}\right.$

DAVE BARRY (b. 1947), a humorist, was recognized for his talent early: he was named Class Clown in his senior year of high school. Barry earned an English degree at Haverford College in 1969; after graduating, he worked as a newspaper reporter for the *Daily Local News* of West Chester, Pennsylvania. He then took a job as a business-writing consultant, but eight years later, in 1983, he returned to print journalism when he joined the *Miami Herald* as a humor columnist. Barry received the Pulitzer Prize for Commentary in 1988, and his columns are now nationally syndicated. His books include *Dave Barry's Complete Guide to Guys* (1991), *Dave Barry Is from Mars AND Venus* (1998), and *Dave Barry's History of the Milennium (So Far)* (2007).

In "A GPS Helps a Guy Always Know Where His Couch Is," first published in the *Miami Herald,* Barry takes a look at electronic gadgetry by means of an old comedy standby: he compares and contrasts the attitudes of men with those of women. As you read, take note of how often Barry ostensibly asserts a position while simultaneously undercutting it with irony, the stuff of which so much humor is made.

———————

I'M A BIG FAN OF technology. Most guys are. This is why all important inventions were invented by guys.

For example, millions of years ago, there was no such thing as the wheel. One day, some primitive guys were watching their wives drag a dead mastodon to the food-preparation area. It was exhausting work; the guys were getting tired just WATCHING. Then they noticed some large, smooth, rounded boulders, and they had an idea: They could sit on the boulders and watch! This was the first in a series of breakthroughs that ultimately led to television.

So we see that there are vital reasons why guys are interested in technology, and why women should not give them a hard time about always wanting to have the "latest gadget." And when I say "women," I mean "my wife."

For example, as a guy, I feel I need a new computer every time a new model comes out, which is every 15 minutes. This baffles my wife, who has had the same computer since the Civil War and refuses to get a new one because—get THIS for an excuse—the one she has works fine. I try to explain that, when you get a new computer, you get exciting new features. My new computer has a truly fascinating feature: Whenever I try to turn it off, the following message, which I am not making up, appears on the screen:

"An exception 0E has occurred at 0028:F000F841 in VxD—. This was called from 0028:C001D324 in VxD NDIS(01) + 00005AA0. It may be possible to continue normally." 5

Clearly, this message is not of human origin. Clearly, my new computer is receiving this message from space aliens. I don't understand all of it, but apparently there has been some kind of intergalactic problem that the aliens want to warn us about. What concerns me is the last sentence, because if the aliens are telling us that "it may be possible to continue normally," they are clearly implying that it may NOT be possible to continue normally. In other words, the Earth may be doomed, and the aliens have chosen ME to receive this message. If I can figure out exactly what they're saying, I might be able to save humanity!

Unfortunately, I don't have time, because I'm busy using my new GPS device. This is an extremely important gadget that every guy in the world needs. It receives signals from orbiting satellites, and somehow— I suspect the "cosine" is involved—it figures out exactly where on the Earth you are. Let's say you're in the town of Arcola, Illinois, but for some reason you do not realize this. You turn on your GPS, and, after pondering for a few minutes, it informs you that you are in . . . Arcola, Illinois! My wife argues that it's easier to just ASK somebody, but of course you cannot do that, if you truly are a guy.

I became aware of how useful a GPS can be when I was on a plane trip with a literary rock band I belong to called the Rock Bottom Remainders, which has been hailed by critics as having one of the world's highest ratios of noise to talent. On this trip were two band members whom I will identify only as "Roger" and "Steve," so that you will not know that they are actually Roger McGuinn, legendary co-founder of the Byrds, and Stephen King, legendary legend.

We were flying from Chicago to Boston, and while everybody else was reading or sleeping, "Roger" and "Steve," who are both fully grown men, were staring at their GPS devices and periodically informing each other how far we were from the Boston airport. "Roger" would say, "I'm showing 238 miles," and "Steve" would say, "I'm showing 241 miles." Then "Roger" would say, "Now I'm showing 236 miles," and "Steve" would come back with another figure, and so on. My wife, who was confident that the airplane pilot did not need help locating Boston, thought this was the silliest thing she had ever seen. Whereas I thought: I NEED one of those.

So I got a GPS for Christmas, and I spent the entire day sitting on a couch, putting it to good use. Like, I figured out exactly where our house is. My wife told me this was exciting news. I think she was being sarcastic, but I couldn't be sure, because I had to keep watching the GPS screen, in case our house moved. I also used my GPS to figure out exactly how far my couch is from LaGuardia Airport (1,103 miles). There is NO END to the usefulness of this device! If you're a guy, you need to get one NOW, so you can locate yourself on the planet. While we still have one.

10

STUDY QUESTIONS

1. According to Barry, why do men want the newest technology? Who does Barry say he means by "women"?

2. COMPARE AND CONTRAST Barry's depictions of men's and women's attitudes toward technology. Why does he call men "guys" but women "women" throughout the article? How seriously does he advocate one perspective over another?

3. *For Writing.* Consider the various electronic devices that you own. Compose an essay in which you REFLECT on how and how often you use them, perhaps comparing and contrasting your use of technology to that of a parent, a sibling, or someone else whose technological skills are markedly different from your own.

JESSICA BENNETT   { *The Flip Side of Internet Fame* }

JESSICA BENNETT (b. 1981) earned a journalism degree from Boston
University and a certificate in cultural anthropology from the University of
Buenos Aires. She has been a reporter for the *Boston Globe,* an investigative
researcher for New York political reporter Wayne Barrett, and a junior
reporter for *Newsweek International.* She is currently an associate editor for
Newsweek magazine, where she writes about culture, technology, and health
for both the print edition and Newsweek.com.

"The Flip Side to Internet Fame" first appeared in *Newsweek* in 2008. In
it, Bennett explores the ethical implications of posting personal information
on the Web—especially personal information about other people. As you
read, consider how posting such material can bring either celebrity or
shame—or both—to the subject of such postings, and whether or not this
is fair.

IN 2002, GHYSLAIN RAZA, A chubby Canadian teen, filmed himself
acting out a fight scene from *Star Wars* using a makeshift light saber.
His awkward performance was funny, in part because it wasn't meant
to be. And it certainly was never meant to be public: for nearly a year
the video remained on a shelf in Raza's school's TV studio, where he'd
filmed it. Sometime in 2003, though, another student discovered the
video, digitized it and posted it online—and Raza's nightmare began.
Within days, "Star Wars Kid" had become a viral frenzy. It was posted
on hundreds of blogs, enhanced by music and special effects, and
watched by millions. Entire Web sites were dedicated to the subject;

one, jedimaster.net, was even named one of *Time*'s 50 best sites of 2003. Had that teenager wanted to be famous, he couldn't have asked for anything better. But in Raza's case it became a source of public humiliation, precisely what every kid fears the most.

Razas of the world take note: among the generation that's been reared online, stories like this are becoming more and more common. They serve as important reminders of a dark side of instant Internet fame: humiliation. Already dozens of Web sites exist solely to help those who would shame others. There are sites for posting hateful rants about ex-lovers (DontDateHimGirl.com) and bad tippers (the S—ty Tipper Database), and for posting cell-phone images of public bad behavior (hollabackNYC.com) and lousy drivers. As a new book makes clear in powerful terms, such sites can make or break a person, in a matter of seconds.

"Anybody can become a celebrity or a worldwide villain in an instant," says Daniel Solove, a law professor at George Washington University and author of *The Future of Reputation: Gossip, Rumor and Privacy on the Internet* (Yale). "Some people may revel in that. But others might say that's not the role they wanted to play in life."

"Dog poop girl" wasn't the public role a South Korean student had in mind when, in 2005, she refused to clean up after her dog in the subway in Seoul. A minor infraction, perhaps, but another passenger captured the act on a cell-phone camera, posted it online and created a viral frenzy. The woman was harassed into dropping out of college. More recently a student at Lewis & Clark University in Portland, Oregon, was publicly accused—on Facebook, the social-networking site—of sexually assaulting another student. Normally, such allegations on campus are kept confidential. But in this case a Facebook group revealed his name, with the word "rapist" for the world to see, before the incident was ever even reported to the authorities. The accused teen was never arrested or charged, but he might as well have been: bloggers picked up the story, and a local alt-weekly put it on its cover, revealing graphic details of the encounter as described by the alleged victim, without including the supposed perpetrator's version of events.

Public shaming, of course, is nothing new. Ancient Romans punished wrongdoers by branding them on the forehead—slaves caught 5 stealing got *fur* (Latin for thief) and runaways got *fug* (fugitive). In Colonial America heretics were clamped into stocks in the public square, thieves had their hands or fingers cut off, and adulterers were forced to wear a scarlet A. More recently a U.S. judge forced a mail thief to wear a sign announcing his crime outside a San Francisco post office; in other places sex offenders have to post warning signs on their front lawns.

Although social stigma can be a useful deterrent, "the Internet is a loose cannon," says ethicist Jim Cohen of Fordham University School of Law in New York. Online there are few checks and balances and no due process—and validating the credibility of a claim is difficult, to say the least. Moreover, studies show that the anonymity of the Net encourages people to say things they normally wouldn't. JuicyCampus, a gossip Web site for U.S. college students, has made headlines by tapping into this urge. The site solicits juicy rumors under the protection of anonymity for sources. But what may have begun as fun and games has turned into a venue for bigoted rants and stories about drug use and sex that identify students by name. "Anyone with a grudge can maliciously and sometimes libelously attack defenseless students," Daniel Belzer, a Duke senior, told *Newsweek* in December.

Regulators find sites like JuicyCampus hard to control. Laws on free speech and defamation vary widely between countries. In the United States, proving libel requires the victim to show that his or her persecutor intended malice, while the British system puts the burden on the defense to show that a statement is not libelous (making it much easier to prosecute). A 1996 U.S. law—Section 230 of the Communications Decency Act—specifically protects the operators of Web sites from liability for the speech of their users. As long as the host of a site doesn't post or edit content, it has no liability. (If AOL,[1] say, were held responsible for every poster, it would quickly go out of business.)

So, then, what's to stop a person from posting whatever he wants about you, if he can do so anonymously and suffer no repercussions? For people who use blogs and social-networking sites like diaries, putting their personal information out there for the world to see, this pres-

---

[1]America Online, an Internet service provider.

ents a serious risk. "I think young people are seduced by the citizen-media notion of the Internet: that everyone can have their minutes of fame," says Barry Schuler, the former CEO of AOL who is now the coproducer of a new movie, *Look,* about public video surveillance. "But they're also putting themselves out there—forever."

Shaming victims, meanwhile, have little legal recourse. Identifying posters often means having to subpoena an anonymous IP address.[2] But that could lead nowhere. Many people share IP addresses on college networks or Wi-Fi hotspots, and many Web sites hide individual addresses. Even if a victim identifies the defamer, bloggers aren't usually rich enough to pay big damage awards. Legal action may only increase publicity—the last thing a shaming victim wants. "The law can only do so much," warns Solove.

Once unsavory information is posted, it's almost impossible to 10 retrieve. The family of the "Star Wars Kid," who spent time in therapy as a result of his ordeal, filed suit against the students who uploaded his video, and settled out of court. But dozens of versions of his video are still widely available, all over the Net. One of the bad boyfriends featured on DontDateHimGirl.com also sued, but his case was dismissed due to lack of jurisdiction. The accused rapist at Lewis & Clark has also hired lawyers. But Google his name today, and the first entry has the word "rapist" in its title. If the "Star Wars Kid" has anything to teach us, it's that shame, like the force, will always be with you.

[2]That is, Internet Protocol address, a numerical identification assigned to each device on a computer network.

STUDY QUESTIONS

1. According to Bennett, what control does an individual have over what personal information is posted online? What are the limits of the law in preventing or punishing those who post information about someone else?

2. Bennett writes that the Internet is a modern tool for the longstanding practice of public shaming. What makes the Internet different from previous ways of public shaming? Does Bennett PERSUADE you that it is more dangerous? Why or why not?

3. *For Writing.* Colleges and universities often counsel students to be mindful of what they post on the Web because of the consequences to their personal or professional lives. Compose an essay in which you explore the ethics of posting information about yourself or someone else on the Web. What guidelines, if any, should be established? How might they be enforced? What should be the legal recourse for victims of online misconduct? Support your ARGUMENT about guidelines with EVIDENCE, either with ANECDOTES about yourself or others you know, or with RESEARCH.

MARK BITTMAN { *I Need a Virtual Break.*
              No, Really.

MARK BITTMAN (b. 1950) is a food writer, cookbook author, and television personality. He writes a weekly cooking column, "The Minimalist," and a regular blog, "Bitten," for the *New York Times*; in addition, he films himself preparing food for the online version of the *Times*. Twice a month he appears on NBC's *Today* show, and he has his own television series on PBS, the third season of which followed famed chef Mario Batali and actress Gwyneth Paltrow on their eating adventures in Spain. Bittman's acclaimed cookbook *How to Cook Everything* (1998) won the IACP/Julia Child award, the James Beard award, and three international cookbook awards; its follow-up, *How to Cook Everything Vegetarian,* was published in 2007. He has also published *Fish: The Complete Guide to Buying and Cooking* (1980) and *The Best Recipes in the World: More Than 1000 International Dishes to Cook at Home* (2005).

Imagine all the computers, cameras, telephones, and other electronic devices that make such a publicly engaged life possible. In the following essay, Bittman reveals his need for a break from technology. After he finds himself "plugging in" even on an airplane, he sets new rules regulating his use of technology—and then he adapts to these rules. Watch for Bittman's use of religious terms and concepts in a thoroughly secular context.

I TOOK A REAL DAY off this weekend: computers shut down, cellphone left in my work bag, land-line ringer off. I was fully disconnected for 24 hours.

The reason for this change was a natural and predictable back-breaking straw. Flying home from Europe a few months ago, I swiped a credit card through the slot of the in-seat phone, checked my e-mail, and robbed myself of one of my two last sanctuaries.

At that point, the only other place I could escape was in my sleep. Yet I had developed the habit of leaving a laptop next to my bed so I could check my e-mail, last thing and first thing. I had learned how to turn my P.D.A. into a modem, the better to access the Web from my laptop when on a train. Of course I also used that P.D.A. in conventional ways, attending to it when it buzzed me.

In short, my name is Mark, and I'm a techno-addict.[1] But after my airplane experience, I decided to do something about it. Thus began my "secular Sabbath"—a term I found floating around on blogs—a day a week where I would be free of screens, bells and beeps. An old-fashioned day not only of rest but of relief.

Like many, though, I wondered whether breaking my habit would be entirely beneficial. I worried about the colleagues, friends, daughters, parents and so on who relied on me, the people who knew that whether I was home or away I would get back to them, if not instantly then certainly before the end of the day. What if something important was happening, something that couldn't wait 24 hours?

Or was I just one of those Americans who've developed the latest in American problems, Internet addiction disorder?

As a baby boomer, I knew mine was no unique thought; we've always been part of some trend or other. And sure enough, as soon as I started looking I found others who felt the need to turn off, to take a stab at reconnecting to things real rather than virtual, a moderate but carefully observed vacation from ubiquitous marketing and the awesome burden of staying in touch.

Nor is this surprising, said David Levy, a professor in the information school at the University of Washington. "What's going on now is insane," he said, assuring me that he used the term intentionally. "Living a good life requires a kind of balance, a bit of quiet. There are questions about the limits of the brain and the body, and there are par-

[1]An allusion to the way members of Alcoholics Anonymous introduce themselves at their meetings.

allels here to the environmental movement." (Dr. Levy coined the term "information environmentalism.")

"Who," he then asked, "would say you don't need time to think, to reflect, to be successful and productive?"

This movement to unplug appears to be gaining traction everywhere, 10 from the blogosphere, where wired types like Ariel Meadow Stallings (http://electrolicious.com/unplugged) brag about turning off the screen one day a week (and how many books they've read so far this year), to the corporate world.

For example, Nathan Zeldes, a principal engineer at Intel (employees there read or send three million e-mail messages daily), is running a couple of experiments, one in which people spend a morning a week at work but offline, another in which people consciously reduce their e-mail output. Though he's not reporting results, he's encouraged and he says people are participating.

"Even many corporate leaders now believe you need time to hear the voice of the new inside," said Anne Dilenschneider, a spirituality consultant in Montara, Calif., a coastal town 17 miles south of San Francisco. "And this time need not be a day, or even a specific period, activity or lack of one. It doesn't necessarily mean a Zen sit, just some time of solitude."

Even without a Zen sit (enough to scare me away from anything) or a phrase like "the voice of the new," I found that the secular Sabbath was not all that easy to maintain. Something as simple as turning off the electronics is easy, but try to make a habit of it.

On my first weekend last fall, I eagerly shut it all down on Friday night, then went to bed to read. (I chose Saturday because my rules include no television, and I had to watch the Giants on Sunday.) I woke up nervous, eager for my laptop. That forbidden, I reached for the phone. No, not that either. Send a text message? No. I quickly realized that I was feeling the same way I do when the electricity goes out and, finding one appliance nonfunctional, I go immediately to the next. I was jumpy, twitchy, uneven.

I managed. I read the whole paper, without hyperlinks. I tried to let 15 myself do nothing, which led to a long, MP3-free walk, a nap and some more reading, an actual novel. I drank herb tea (caffeine was not helpful) and stared out the window. I tried to allow myself to be less purposeful, not to care what was piling up in my personal cyberspace, and not to think about how busy I was going to be the next morning. I cooked, then went to bed, and read some more.

Gradually, over this and the next couple of weekends—one of which stretched from Friday night until Monday morning, like the old days—I adapted.

But recidivism quickly followed; there were important things to do—deadlines, urgent communications. You know how it is. I called Andrea Bauer, an executive and career development coach in San Carlos, Calif. She assured me that, oddly enough, it takes work to stop working. "It takes different formats for different people, and you have to build up to it; you can't run five miles if you've never run at all." Increasingly, I realized that there is more to the secular Sabbath than an impulse, or even a day off from e-mail. And there are reasons that nonsecular Sabbaths—the holy days of Christians, Jews and Muslims—have rules that require discipline. Even for the nonreligious, those rules were once imposed: You need not be elderly to remember when we had no choice but to reduce activity on Sundays; stores and offices—even restaurants—were closed, there were certainly no electronics, and we were largely occupied by ourselves or our families.

Now it's up to us, and, as Dr. Levy says, there's little encouragement. "One of the problems with needing to slow down is that within the climate of our primary culture it sounds wishy-washy," he said.

But what's wishy-washy about taking time off? It didn't seem to me that I had to collect Social Security before I realized that a 70-hour week was nearly as productive as an 80-hour one, and if I couldn't get it all done in either, it certainly wasn't because I was taking too much time off.

I went back to nonwork, diligently following my rules to do less one day a week. The walks, naps and reading became routine, and all as enjoyable as they were before I had to force myself into doing them. It's been more than six months, and while I'm hardly a new man—no one has yet called me mellow—this achievement is unlike any other in my life. And nothing bad has happened while I've been offline; the e-mail and phone messages, RSS feeds, are all there waiting for me when I return to them.

I would no more make a new-agey call to find inner peace than I would encourage a return to the mimeograph. But I do believe that there has to be a way to regularly impose some thoughtfulness, or at least calm, into modern life—or at least my version. Once I moved beyond the fear of being unavailable and what it might cost me, I experienced what, if I wasn't such a skeptic, I would call a lightness of being. I felt connected to myself rather than my computer. I had time to think, and distance from normal demands. I got to stop.

STUDY QUESTIONS

1. Why does Bittman say he needs to take a break from technology? Why is it difficult for him to turn off his gadgets? What does his "break" consist of—that is, what rules does he set for himself? How successful is he?

2. What are some of the REASONS that Bittman cites for reducing the amount of time he spends engaging with technology? What kinds of EVIDENCE does he supply to support those reasons? How effectively does he make his point?

3. *For Writing.* Drawing on your own experience, write a PERSONAL ESSAY in which you advocate for being plugged in, unplugged, or a particular combination of both. What are the benefits to your solution? What are the drawbacks?

RACHEL CARSON { *The Obligation to Endure*

RACHEL CARSON (1907–1964) was born in Springdale, Pennsylvania, graduated from Pennsylvania College for Women in 1929, and received her MA in zoology from Johns Hopkins University in 1932. After writing three books on oceanic topics, she refocused her attention to the effects of pesticides on humans and the environment. In 1962 she published *Silent Spring*, a work that explained the way chemicals affect the ecosystem and helped launch the modern environmentalism movement. Before her death from breast cancer she testified in congressional hearings and called for new policies to regulate chemicals in the environment and to protect human health.

In this chapter from *Silent Spring*, Carson translates her research into accessible prose. She begins by presenting information, but she gradually produces so much evidence to support her claims that her expository writing subtly takes on a persuasive tone, revealing the dangers that humanity both creates and experiences when using chemicals to control the environment.

THE HISTORY OF LIFE ON earth has been a history of interaction between living things and their surroundings. To a large extent, the physical form and the habits of the earth's vegetation and its animal life have been molded by the environment. Considering the whole span of earthly time, the opposite effect, in which life actually modifies its surroundings, has been relatively slight. Only within the moment of time represented by the present century has one species—man—acquired significant power to alter the nature of his world.

During the past quarter century this power has not only increased to one of disturbing magnitude but it has changed in character. The most alarming of all man's assaults upon the environment is the contamination of air, earth, rivers, and sea with dangerous and even lethal materials. This pollution is for the most part irrecoverable; the chain of evil it initiates not only in the world that must support life but in living tissues is for the most part irreversible. In this now universal contamination of the environment, chemicals are the sinister and little-recognized partners of radiation in changing the very nature of the world—the very nature of its life. Strontium 90, released through nuclear explosions into the air, comes to earth in rain or drifts down as fallout, lodges in soil, enters into the grass or corn or wheat grown there, and in time takes up its abode in the bones of a human being, there to remain until his death. Similarly, chemicals sprayed on croplands or forests or gardens lie long in soil, entering into living organisms, passing from one to another in a chain of poisoning and death. Or they pass mysteriously by underground streams until they emerge and, through the alchemy of air and sunlight, combine into new forms that kill vegetation, sicken cattle, and work unknown harm on those who drink from once-pure wells. As Albert Schweitzer[1] has said, "Man can hardly even recognize the devils of his own creation."

It took hundreds of millions of years to produce the life that now inhabits the earth—eons of time in which that developing and evolving and diversifying life reached a state of adjustment and balance with its surroundings. The environment, rigorously shaping and directing the life it supported, contained elements that were hostile as well as supporting. Certain rocks gave out dangerous radiation; even within the light of the sun, from which all life draws its energy, there were short-wave radiations with power to injure. Given time—time not in years but in millennia—life adjusts, and a balance has been reached. For time is the essential ingredient; but in the modern world there is no time.

[1]French-German doctor (1875-1965) and philosopher.

The rapidity of change and the speed with which new situations are created follow the impetuous and the heedless pace of man rather than the deliberate pace of nature. Radiation is no longer merely the background radiation of rocks, the bombardment of cosmic rays, the ultraviolet of the sun that have existed before there was any life on earth; radiation is now the unnatural creation of man's tampering with the atom. The chemicals to which life is asked to make its adjustment are no longer merely the calcium and silica and copper and all the rest of the minerals washed out of the rocks and carried in rivers to the sea; they are the synthetic creations of man's inventive mind, brewed in his laboratories, and having no counterparts in nature.

To adjust to these chemicals would require time on the scale that is 5 nature's; it would require not merely the years of a man's life but the life of generations. And even this, were it by some miracle possible, would be futile, for the new chemicals come from our laboratories in an endless stream; almost 500 annually find their way into actual use in the United States alone. The figure is staggering and its implications are not easily grasped—500 new chemicals to which the bodies of men and animals are required somehow to adapt each year, chemicals totally outside the limits of biologic experience.

Among them are many that are used in man's war against nature. Since the mid-1940's over 200 basic chemicals have been created for use in killing insects, weeds, rodents, and other organisms described in the modern vernacular as "pests"; and they are sold under several thousand different brand names.

These sprays, dusts, and aerosols are now applied almost universally to farms, gardens, forests, and homes—nonselective chemicals that have the power to kill every insect, the "good" and the "bad," to still the song of birds and the leaping of fish in the streams, to coat the leaves with a deadly film, and to linger on in soil—all this though the intended target may be only a few weeds or insects. Can anyone believe it is possible to lay down such a barrage of poisons on the surface of the earth without making it unfit for all life? They should not be called "insecticides," but "biocides."

The whole process of spraying seems caught up in an endless spiral. Since DDT[2] was released for civilian use, a process of escalation has been going on in which ever more toxic materials must be found. This has happened because insects, in a triumphant vindication of Darwin's principle of the survival of the fittest, have evolved super races immune to the particular insecticide used, hence a deadlier one has always to be developed—and then a deadlier one than that. It has happened also because, for reasons to be described later, destructive insects often undergo a "flareback," or resurgence, after spraying, in numbers greater than before. Thus the chemical war is never won, and all life is caught in its violent crossfire.

Along with the possibility of the extinction of mankind by nuclear war, the central problem of our age has therefore become the contamination of man's total environment with such substances of incredible potential for harm—substances that accumulate in the tissues of plants and animals and even penetrate the germ cells to shatter or alter the very material of heredity upon which the shape of the future depends.

Some would-be architects of our future look toward a time when it will be possible to alter the human germ plasm by design. But we may easily be doing so now by inadvertence, for many chemicals, like radiation, bring about gene mutations. It is ironic to think that man might determine his own future by something so seemingly trivial as the choice of an insect spray.

All this has been risked—for what? Future historians may well be amazed by our distorted sense of proportion. How could intelligent beings seek to control a few unwanted species by a method that contaminated the entire environment and brought the threat of disease and death even to their own kind? Yet this is precisely what we have done. We have done it, moreover, for reasons that collapse the moment we examine them. We are told that the enormous and expanding use of pesticides is necessary to maintain farm production. Yet is our real problem not one of *overproduction?* Our farms, despite measures to remove acreages from production and to pay farmers *not* to produce,

[2]Dichloro-Diphenyl-Trichloroethane, a synthetic pesticide banned in the United States in 1972.

29

have yielded such a staggering excess of crops that the American tax-payer in 1962 is paying out more than one billion dollars a year as the total carrying cost of the surplus-food storage program. And is the situation helped when one branch of the Agriculture Department tries to reduce production while another states, as it did in 1958, "It is believed generally that reduction of crop acreages under provisions of the Soil Bank will stimulate interest in use of chemicals to obtain maximum production on the land retained in crops"?

All this is not to say there is no insect problem and no need of control. I am saying, rather, that control must be geared to realities, not to mythical situations, and that the methods employed must be such that they do not destroy us along with the insects.

• ○ •

The problem whose attempted solution has brought such a train of disaster in its wake is an accompaniment of our modern way of life. Long before the age of man, insects inhabited the earth—a group of extraordinarily varied and adaptable beings. Over the course of time since man's advent, a small percentage of the more than half a million species of insects have come into conflict with human welfare in two principal ways: as competitors for the food supply and as carriers of human disease.

Disease-carrying insects become important where human beings are crowded together, especially under conditions where sanitation is poor, as in time of natural disaster or war or in situations of extreme poverty and deprivation. Then control of some sort becomes necessary. It is a sobering fact, however, as we shall presently see, that the method of massive chemical control has had only limited success, and also threatens to worsen the very conditions it is intended to curb.

Under primitive agricultural conditions the farmer had few insect 15 problems. These arose with the intensification of agriculture—the devotion of immense acreages to a single crop. Such a system set the stage for explosive increases in specific insect populations. Single-crop farming does not take advantage of the principles by which nature works; it is agriculture as an engineer might conceive it to be. Nature has introduced great variety into the landscape, but man has displayed a passion for simplifying it. Thus he undoes the built-in checks and balances by which nature holds the species within bounds. One important natural check is a limit on the amount of suitable habitat for each species. Obviously then, an insect that lives on wheat can build up its population to much higher levels on a farm devoted to wheat than on one in which wheat is intermingled with other crops to which the insect is not adapted.

The same thing happens in other situations. A generation or more ago, the towns of large areas of the United States lined their streets with the noble elm tree. Now the beauty they hopefully created is threatened with complete destruction as disease sweeps through the elms, carried by a beetle that would have only limited chance to build up large populations and to spread from tree to tree if the elms were only occasional trees in a richly diversified planting.

Another factor in the modern insect problem is one that must be viewed against a background of geologic and human history: the spreading of thousands of different kinds of organisms from their native homes to invade new territories. This worldwide migration has been studied and graphically described by the British ecologist Charles Elton in his recent book *The Ecology of Invasions*. During the Cretaceous Period, some hundred million years ago, flooding seas cut many land bridges between continents and living things found themselves confined in what Elton calls "colossal separate nature reserves." There, isolated from others of their kind, they developed many new species. When some of the land masses were joined again, about 16 million years ago, these species began to move out into new territories—a movement that is not only still in progress but is now receiving considerable assistance from man.

The importation of plants is the primary agent in the modern spread of species, for animals have almost invariably gone along with the plants, quarantine being a comparatively recent and not completely effective innovation. The United States Office of Plant Introduction alone has introduced almost 200,000 species and varieties of plants from all over the world. Nearly half of the 180 or so major insect enemies of plants in the United States are accidental imports from abroad, and most of them have come as hitchhikers on plants. In new territory, out of reach of the restraining hand of the natural enemies that kept down its numbers in its native land, an invading plant or animal is able to become enormously abundant. Thus it is no accident that our most troublesome insects are introduced species.

These invasions, both the naturally occurring and those dependent on human assistance, are likely to continue indefinitely. Quarantine and massive chemical campaigns are only extremely expensive ways of buying time. We are faced, according to Dr. Elton, "with a life-and-death need not just to find new technological means of suppressing this plant or that animal"; instead we need the basic knowledge of animal populations and their relations to their surroundings that will "promote an even balance and damp down the explosive power of outbreaks and new invasions." Much of the necessary knowledge is now available but we do not use it. We train ecologists in our universities and even employ them in our governmental agencies but we seldom take their advice. We allow the chemical death rain to fall as though there were no alternative, whereas in fact there are many, and our ingenuity could soon discover many more if given opportunity.

Have we fallen into a mesmerized state that makes us accept as 20 inevitable that which is inferior or detrimental, as though having lost the will or the vision to demand that which is good? Such thinking, in the words of the ecologist Paul Shepard, "idealizes life with only its head out of water, inches above the limits of toleration of the corruption of its own environment. . . . Why should we tolerate a diet of weak poisons, a home in insipid surroundings, a circle of acquaintances who are not quite our enemies, the noise of motors with just enough relief to prevent insanity? Who would want to live in a world which is just not quite fatal?"

Yet such a world is pressed upon us. The crusade to create a chemically sterile, insect-free world seems to have engendered a fanatic zeal on the part of many specialists and most of the so-called control agencies. On every hand there is evidence that those engaged in spraying operations exercise a ruthless power. "The regulatory entomologists . . . function as prosecutor, judge and jury, tax assessor and collector and sheriff to enforce their own orders," said Connecticut entomologist Neely Turner. The most flagrant abuses go unchecked in both state and federal agencies.

It is not my contention that chemical insecticides must never be used. I do contend that we have put poisonous and biologically potent chemicals indiscriminately into the hands of persons largely or wholly ignorant of their potentials for harm. We have subjected enormous numbers of people to contact with these poisons, without their consent and often without their knowledge. If the Bill of Rights contains no guarantee that a citizen shall be secure against lethal poisons distributed either by private individuals or by public officials, it is surely only because our forefathers, despite their considerable wisdom and foresight, could conveive of no such problem.

I contend, furthermore, that we have allowed these chemicals to be used with little or no advance investigation of their effect on soil, water, wildlife, and man himself. Future generations are unlikely to condone our lack of prudent concern for the integrity of the natural world that supports all life.

There is still very limited awareness of the nature of the threat. This is an era of specialists, each of whom sees his own problem and is unaware of or intolerant of the larger frame into which it fits. It is also an era dominated by industry, in which the right to make a dollar at whatever cost is seldom challenged. When the public protests, confronted with some obvious evidence of damaging results of pesticide applications, it is fed little tranquilizing pills of half-truth. We urgently need an end to these false assurances, to the sugar coating of unpalatable facts. It is the public that is being asked to assume the risks that the insect controllers calculate. The public must decide whether it wishes to continue on the present road, and it can do so only when in full possession of the facts. In the words of Jean Rostand,[3] "The obligation to endure gives us the right to know."

[3]French biologist and philosopher (1894–1977).

STUDY QUESTIONS

1. According to Carson, "the history of life on earth has been a history of interaction between living things and their surroundings." However, humanity's presence has changed this interaction in fundamental ways. Explain what she means. How have human beings affected life on earth?

2. Characterize Carson's TONE. Is her language overtly PERSUASIVE or more EXPOSITORY? How would you use language to make CLAIMS similar to those Carson makes? Choose one section of the essay in which she writes about dangers to life, and rewrite it to reflect your own writing style.

3. Reread paragraph 2. Carson uses some strong language to convince the reader about humanity's part in harming the environment. Identify the key sentence that presents her THESIS, and show how she supports her claim in that paragraph and in the following paragraphs. Has she convinced you? Explain.

4. *For Writing.* Visit your local grocery store, hardware store, drugstore, or other store that sells items that contain chemicals, such as hair spray, hair dyes, insecticides, fertilizers, and paint removers. Choose a category of items—e.g., cosmetics or pesticides—to examine thoroughly. Read not only the ingredients but also any warnings that are on the labels. RESEARCH the ingredients of the products you have chosen. Write an expository or a persuasive essay about the dangers found in everyday products that Carson did not mention in her chapter.

RICHARD CONNIFF { *Why Did God Make Flies?*

RICHARD CONNIFF (b. 1951) has written about leeches, snapping turtles, tarantulas, jellyfish, and even humans. He didn't start out intending to write about the natural world, and only discovered a genuine interest in it when assigned to write a piece about the salt marsh mosquito in his mid-twenties. Conniff, who wasn't a biology major while an undergraduate at Yale University, approaches his subjects with a genuine and contagious fascination. He has written for magazines such as *Time, National Geographic,* and *Smithsonian* and is the author of several books, including *Swimming with Piranhas at Feeding Time: My Life Doing Dumb Stuff with Animals* (2009), *The Natural History of the Rich: A Field Guide* (2002), and *Spineless Wonders: Strange Tales from the Invertebrate World* (1996). Along the way he has traveled the world and won many awards, including a Guggenheim Fellowship in 2007 and a Loeb Journalism Award in 2009.

In this essay from *Spineless Wonders,* Conniff examines what he calls a "fantastic animal"—otherwise known as the fly. The essay opens with his consideration of a housefly that has landed on the rim of his beer glass. This unusual beginning leads to a careful and lively examination of not just the common housefly, but its influence on the human world and, surprisingly, the human world's influence on the fly. As you read the essay, pay attention to the way Conniff makes complicated technical information both easy to understand and memorable.

THOUGH I HAVE BEEN KILLING them for years now, I have never tested the notion, recorded in one collection of country sayings, that with a little cream and sugar, a fly "tastes very much like a black raspberry." So it's possible I'm speaking too hastily when I say there is nothing to like about flies. Unlike the poet who welcomed a "busy, curious fly"[1] to his drinking cup, I don't cherish them for reminding me that life is short. Nor do I much admire them for their function in clearing away carrion and waste. It is, after all, possible to believe in the grand scheme of recycling without necessarily liking undertakers.

Among poets, I tend to side with Ogden Nash,[2] who once wrote: "God in His wisdom / Made the fly / And then forgot / To tell us why."

A fly is standing on the rim of my beer glass as I write these words. Its vast, mosaic eyes look simultaneously lifeless and mocking. It grooms itself methodically, its forelegs twining together like the arms of a Sybarite[3] luxuriating in bath oil. Its hind legs twitch across the upper surface of its wings. It pauses, well-fed and at rest, to contemplate the sweetness of life.

We are lucky enough to live in an era when scientists quantify such things, and so as I type and wait my turn to drink, I know that the fly is neither busy nor curious; the female spends 40.6 percent of her time doing nothing but contemplating the sweetness of life. I know that she not only eats unspeakable things, but that she spends an additional 29.7 percent of her time spitting them back up again and blowing bubbles with her vomit. The male is slightly less assiduous at this deplorable pastime, but one diligent researcher has reported that a well-fed fly may also defecate every four and a half minutes. Flies seldom trouble us as a health threat anymore, at least in the developed world, but they are capable of killing. And when we are dead (or sooner, in some cases), they dine on our corrupted flesh.

---

[1] English author William Oldys (1687–1761), better known as a rare book collector and bibliographer.

[2] American poet (1902–71) known for his light verse.

[3] One who enjoys luxuries, after the inhabitants of the sixth-century Greek city of Sybaris, famous seekers of pleasure.

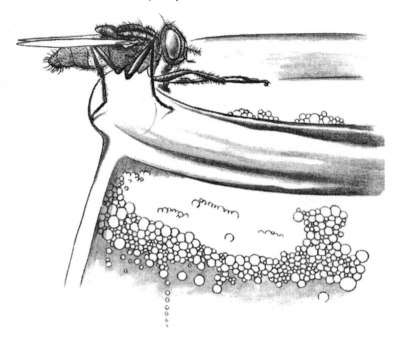

It is of course mainly this relentless intimacy with mankind that   5
makes flies and particularly houseflies so contemptible. Leeches or
dung beetles may appall us, but by and large they satisfy their depraved
appetites out of our sight. Flies, on the other hand, routinely flit from
diaper pail to dinner table, from carrion to picnic basket. They are
constantly among us, tramping across our food with God knows what
trapped in the sticky hairs of their half-dozen legs.

Twice in this century, Americans have waged war against flies,
once in a futile nationwide "swat the fly" campaign, and again, disas-
trously, with DDT[4] foggings after World War II. The intensity of
these efforts, bordering at times on the fanatic, may bewilder modern
readers. "Flies or Babies? Choose!" cried a headline in the *Ladies'
Home Journal*, in 1920. But our bewilderment is not entirely due to

---

[4] Synthetic pesticide used from the mid 20th century until its ban, in 1972 by the United
States, and somewhat later in the rest of the world. Its widespread use threatened many
forms of wildlife, in particular birds.

greater tolerance or environmental enlightenment. If we have the leisure to examine the fly more rationally now, it is mainly because we don't suffer its onslaughts as our predecessors did. Urban living has separated us from livestock, and indoor plumbing has helped us control our own wastes, thus controlling flies. But if that changed tomorrow, we would come face-to-face with the enlightened, modern truth: With the possible exception of *Homo sapiens*, it is hard to imagine an animal as disgusting or improbable as the housefly. No bestiary concocted out of the nightmares of the medieval mind could have come up with such a fantastic animal. If we want to study nature in its most exotic permutations, the best place to begin is here, at home, on the rim of my beer glass.

In North America, more than a dozen fly species visit or live in the house. It is possible to distinguish among some of them only by such microscopic criteria as the pattern of veins in the wings, and so all of them end up being cursed as houseflies. Among the more prominent are the blue and the green bottleflies, with their iridescent abdomens, and the biting stable flies, which have served this country as patriots, or at least as provocateurs. On July 4, 1776, their biting encouraged decisiveness among delegates considering the Declaration of Independence: "Treason," Thomas Jefferson wrote, "was preferable to discomfort."

The true housefly, *Musca domestica*, of course does not bite. (You may think this is something to like about flies, until you find out what they do instead.) *M. domestica*, a drab fellow of salt-and-pepper complexion, is the world's most widely distributed insect species and probably also the most familiar, a status achieved through its pronounced fondness for breeding in pig, horse, or human excrement. In choosing at some point in the immemorial past to concentrate on the wastes around human habitations, *M. domestica* made a brilliant career move. The earliest known human representation of what appears to be a housefly is on a Mesopotamian cylinder seal from 3000 B.C.[5] But

---

[5] Somewhat later, the ancient Romans used a poultice of mashed houseflies as a treatment for baldness. Flies are hairy, and the theory was that it might rub off on bald men. [Author's note]

houseflies were probably with us even before we had houses, and they spread with human culture.

Like us, the housefly is prolific, opportunistic, and inclined toward exploration. It can adapt to either vegetable or meat diets, preferably somewhat ripe. It will lay its eggs not just in excrement, but in a rotting mass of lime peels, in bird nests, in carrion, or even in flesh wounds that have become infected and malodorous. Other flies aren't so flexible. For instance, *M. autumnalis*, a close relative, prefers cattle dung, and winds up sleeping in the pasture more than in houses or yards.

But while the housefly's adaptability and evolutionary generaliza- 10 tion may be admirable, it raises one of the first great questions about flies: Why this dismaying appetite for abomination?

Houseflies not only defecate constantly, but do so in liquid form, which means they are in constant danger of dehydration. The male can slake his thirst and also get most of the energy he needs from nectar. But fresh manure is a good source of water, and it contains the dissolved protein the female needs to make eggs. She also lays her eggs in excrement or amid decay so that when they hatch, the maggots will have a smorgasbord of numerous microorganisms on which to graze.

Houseflies bashing around the kitchen or the garbage shed thus have their sensors attuned to things that smell sweet, like flowers or bananas, and to foul-smelling stuff like ammonium carbonate, hydrogen sulfide, and trimethylamines, the products of fermentation and putrefaction. (Ecstasy for the fly is the stinkhorn fungus, a source of sugar that smells like rotting meat.) The fly's jerky, erratic flight amounts to a way of covering large territories in search of these scents, not just for food, but for romance and breeding sites. Like dung beetles and other flying insects, the fly will zigzag upwind when it gets a whiff of something good (or, as often happens, something bad) and follow the scent plume to its source.

Hence the second diabolical question about the housefly: How does it manage to fly so well? Why is it so adept at evading us when we swat it? How come it always seems to land on its feet, usually upside down on the ceiling, having induced us to plant a fist on the spot where it used to be, in the middle of the strawberry trifle, which is now spattered across tablecloth, walls, loved ones, and honored guests?

When we launch an ambush as the oblivious fly preens and pukes, its pressure sensors alert it to the speed and direction of the descending hand. Its wraparound eyes are also acutely sensitive to peripheral movement, and they register changes in light about ten times faster than we do. (A movie fools the gullible human eye into seeing continuous motion by showing it a sequence of twenty-four still pictures a second. To fool a fly would take more than two hundred frames a second.) The alarm flashes directly from the brain to the middle set of legs via the largest, and therefore the fastest, nerve fiber in the body. This causes so-called starter muscles to contract, simultaneously revving up the wing muscles and pressing down the middle legs, which catapult the fly into the air.

The fly's wings beat 165 to 200 times a second, and while this isn't   15
all that fast for an insect, it's more than double the wingbeat of the fastest hummingbird, and about 20 times faster than any repetitious movement the human nervous system can manage. The trick brought off by houseflies and many other insects is to remove the wingbeat from direct nervous system control, once it's switched on. Instead, two systems of muscles, for upstroke and downstroke, are attached to the hull of the fly's midsection, and trigger each other to work in alternation. When one set contracts, it deforms the hull, stretching the other set of muscles and making them contract automatically a fraction of a second later. To keep this seesaw rhythm going, openings in the midsection stoke the muscles with oxygen directly from the outside (the fly has no lungs). Its blood (which lacks hemoglobin and is therefore colorless) meanwhile pumps fuel for the cells to burn at a rate 14 times faster than when the fly is at rest. Flies can turn a sugar meal into usable energy so fast that an exhausted fly will resume flight almost instantly after eating. In humans . . . but you don't want to know how ploddingly inadequate humans are by comparison.

Once airborne, the fly's antennae, between its eyes, help regulate flight, vibrating in response to airflow. The fly also uses a set of stubby wings in back, called halteres, as a gyroscopic device. Flies are skillful at veering and dodging; it sometimes seems that they are doing barrel rolls and Immelmann turns[6] to amuse themselves while we flail and curse. But one thing they cannot do is fly upside down to land on a ceiling. This phenomenon puzzled generations of upward-glaring, strawberry-trifle-drenched human beings, until high-speed photography supplied the explanation. The fly approaches the ceiling right-side up, at a steep angle. Just before impact, it reaches up with its front limbs, in the manner of Superman exiting a telephone booth for take-off. As these forelegs get a grip with claws and with the sticky, glandular hairs of the footpads, the fly swings its other legs up into position. Then it shuts down its flight motor, out of swatting range and at ease.

While landing on the ceiling must be great fun, humans tend to be more interested in what flies do when they land on food, and so I trapped the fly on the rim of my beer glass. (Actually, I waited till it found a less coveted perch, then slowly lowered a mayonnaise jar over it.) I'd been reading a book called *To Know a Fly* by Vincent Dethier, in which he describes a simple way of seeing how the fly's proboscis works. First, I refrigerated the fly to slow it down and anesthetize it. Then I attempted to attach a thin stick to its wing surface with the help of hot wax. It got away. I brought it back and tried again. My son Jamie, who was then four years old, winced and turned aside when I applied the wax. "I'm glad I'm not a fly," he said, "or you might do that to me." I regarded him balefully but refrained from mentioning the ant colony he had annihilated on our front walk.

Having finally secured the fly, I lowered its feet into a saucer of water. Flies have taste buds in their feet, and when they walk into something good (bad), the proboscis, which is normally folded up neatly inside the head, automatically flicks down. No response. I added sugar to the water, an irresistible combination. Nothing. More sugar. Still nothing. My son wandered off, bored. I apologized to the fly, killed it, and decided to look up the man who had put me in the awkward position of sympathizing with a fly, incidentally classing me in my son's eyes as a potential war criminal.

Dethier, a biologist at the University of Massachusetts, turned out to be a gentle, deferential fellow in his mid-seventies, with weathered,

---

[6] Aerobatic maneuvers in which a plane ascends and rolls.

finely wrinkled skin and a pair of gold-rimmed oval eyeglasses on a
beak nose. He suggested mildly that my fly might not have responded
because it was outraged at the treatment it received. It may also have
eaten recently, or it may have been groggy from hibernation. (Some flies
sit out the winter in diapause, in which hormones induce inactivity in
response to shortened day length. But cold, not day length, is what
slows down hibernating species like the housefly, and the sudden
return of warmth can start them up again. This is why a fly may miracu-
lously take wing on a warm December afternoon in the space between
my closed office window and the closed storm window outside, a phenomenon I had formerly regarded as new evidence for spontaneous
generation.) Dethier has spent a lifetime studying the fly's sense of
taste, "finding out where their tongues and noses are, as it were." He
explained the workings of the proboscis for me.

Fly taste buds are vastly more sensitive than ours, another reason 20
to dislike them. Dethier figured this out by taking saucers of water
containing steadily decreasing concentrations of sugar. He found the
smallest concentration a human tongue could taste. Then he found
the smallest concentration that caused a hungry fly to flick out its proboscis. The fly, with fifteen hundred taste hairs arrayed on its feet and
in and around its mouth, was ten million times more sensitive.

When the fly hits paydirt, the proboscis telescopes downward and
the fleshy lobes at the tip puff out. These lips can press down tight to
feed on a thin film of liquid, or they can cup themselves around a
droplet. They are grooved crosswise with a series of parallel gutters,
and when the fly starts pumping, the liquid gets drawn up through
these gutters. The narrow zigzag openings of the gutters filter the food,
so that even when it dines on excrement, the fly can "choose" some
microorganisms and reject others. A drop of vomit may help dissolve
the food, making it easier to lap up. Scientists have also suggested that
the fly's prodigious vomiting may be a way of mixing enzymes with the
food to aid digestion.

If necessary, the fly can peel its lips back out of the way and apply
its mouth directly to the object of its desire. While it does not have
true teeth, the mouth of the housefly is lined with a jagged, bladelike
edge, which is useful for scraping. In his book *Flies and Disease*, Ber-

nard Greenberg, a forensic entomologist at the University of Illinois in Chicago, writes that some blowflies (like the one on the rim of my beer glass, which turned out to be an olive green blowfly, *Phormia regina*) "can bring one hundred fifty teeth into action, a rather effective scarifier for the superficial inoculation of the skin, conjunctiva, or mucous membranes."

Hence the final great question about flies: What awful things are they inoculating us with when they flit across our food or land on our sleeping lips to drink our saliva? Over the years, authorities have suspected flies of spreading more than sixty diseases, from diarrhea to plague and leprosy. As recently as 1951, the leading expert on flies repeated without demurring the idea that the fly was "the most dangerous insect known," a remarkable assertion in a world that also includes mosquitoes. One entomologist tried to have the housefly renamed the "typhoid fly."

The hysteria against flies early in this century arose, with considerable help from scientists and the press, out of the combined ideas that germs cause disease and that flies carry germs. In the Spanish-American War, easily ten times as many soldiers died of disease, mostly typhoid fever, as died in battle. Flies were widely blamed, especially after a doctor observed particles of faces picked up in the latrines still clinging to the legs of flies crawling over army food. Flies were not "dipterous angels,"[7] but "winged sponges speeding hither and thither to carry out the foul behests of Contagion." North American schools started organizing "junior sanitary police" to point the finger at fly-breeding sites. Cities sponsored highly publicized "swat the fly" campaigns. In Toronto in 1912, a girl named Beatrice White killed 543,360 flies, altogether weighing 212.25 pounds, and won a $50 first prize. This is a mess of flies, 108.7 swatted for every penny in prize money, testimony to the slowness of summers then and to the remarkable agility of children—or perhaps to the overzealous imagination of contest sponsors. The figure does not include the 2.8 million

---

[7] In an 1871 article in the *London Lancet* Lord Avebury said that flies must not be seen simply as "dipterous angels." Diptera is a large order of insects, including flies, characterized by having one pair of membranous wings and another pair of winglike balancing organs.

dead flies submitted by losing entrants. (The "swat the fly" spirit still lives in China. In 1992, Beijing issued 200,000 flyswatters and launched a major sanitation campaign under the slogan, "Mobilize the Masses to Build a City of No Flies.")

But it took the pesticide DDT, developed in World War II and 25 touted afterward as "the killer of killers," to raise the glorious prospect of "a flyless millennium." The fly had by then been enshrined in the common lore as a diabolical killer. In one of the "archy and mehitabel" poems by Don Marquis,[8] a fly visits garbage cans and sewers to "gather up the germs of typhoid influenza and pneumonia on my feet and wings" and spread them to humanity, declaring "it is my mission to help rid the world of these wicked persons / i am a vessel of righteousness."

Public health officials were deadly serious about conquering this archfiend, and for them DDT was "a veritable godsend." They recommended that parents use wallpaper impregnated with DDT in nurseries and playrooms to protect children. Cities suffering polio epidemics frequently used airplanes to fog vast areas "in the belief that the fly factor in the spread of infantile paralysis might thus be largely eliminated." Use of DDT actually provided some damning evidence against flies, though not in connection with polio. Hidalgo County in Texas, on the Mexican border, divided its towns into two groups, and sprayed one with DDT to eliminate flies. The number of children suffering and dying from acute diarrheal infection caused by *Shigella* bacteria declined in the sprayed areas but remained the same in the unsprayed areas. When DDT spraying was stopped in the first group and switched to the second, the dysentery rates began to reverse. Then the flies developed resistance to DDT, a small hitch in the godsend. In state parks and vacation spots, where DDT had provided relief from the fly nuisance, people began to notice that songbirds were also disappearing.

[8] Don Marquis (1878–1937) was an American humorist who created a newspaper column supposedly written on a typewriter by a cockroach, Archy, whose best friend was a cat named Mehitabel. In the column, which ran in the *New York Evening Sun* in the 1910s and 1920s, Archy wrote poems and stories and narrated his daily adventures with Mehitabel.

In the end, the damning evidence was that we were contaminating our water, ourselves, and our affiliated population of flies with our own filth (not to mention DDT). Given access to human waste through inadequate plumbing or sewage treatment, flies can indeed pick up an astonishing variety of pathogens. They can also reproduce at a god-awful rate; in one study, 4,042 flies hatched from a scant shovelful, one-sixth of a cubic foot, of buried night soil. But whether all those winged sponges can transmit the contaminants they pick up turns out to be a tricky question, the Hidalgo County study being one of the few clear-cut exceptions. Of polio, for instance, Bernard Greenberg writes, "there is ample evidence that human populations readily infect flies. . . . But we are woefully ignorant whether and to what extent flies return the favor."

Flies thus probably are not, as one writer declared in the throes of the hysteria, "monstrous" beings "armed with horrid mandibles . . . and dripping poison." A fly's bristling unlovely body is not, after all, a playground for microbes. Indeed, bacterial populations on the fly's exterior tend to decline quickly under the triple threat of compulsive cleaning, desiccation, and ultraviolet radiation. (Maggots actually produce a substance in their gut that kills off whole populations of bacteria, which is one reason doctors have sometimes used them to clean out infected wounds.) The fly's "microbial cargo," to use Greenberg's phrase, tends to reflect human uncleanliness. In one study, flies from a city neighborhood with poor facilities carried up to 500 million bacteria, while flies from a prim little suburb not far away yielded a maximum count of only 100,000.

But wait. While I am perfectly happy to suggest that humans are viler than we like to think, and flies less so, I do not mean to rehabilitate the fly. Any animal that kisses offal one minute and dinner the next is at the very least a social abomination. What I am coming around to is St. Augustine's[9] idea that God created flies to punish human arrogance, and not just the calamitous technological arrogance of DDT. Flies are, as one biologist has remarked, the resurrection and the reincarnation of our own dirt, and this is surely one reason we smite them down with

---

[9] Augustine (354–430), Bishop of Hippo, was a philosopher who lived in north Africa. His *Confessions* documents his difficult conversion to Christianity.

such ferocity. They mock our notions of personal grooming with visions of lime particles, night soil,[1] and dog leavings. They toy with our delusions of immortality, buzzing in the ear as a memento mori.[2] (Dr. Greenberg assures me that fly maggots can strip a human corpse roughly halfway to the bone in several weeks, if the weather is fine. Then they hand the job over to other insects.) Flies are our fate, and one way or another they will have us.

It is a pretty crummy joke on God's part, of course, but there's no   30 point in getting pouty about it and slipping into unhealthy thoughts about nature. What I intend to do, by way of evening the score, is hang a strip of flypaper and also cultivate the local frogs and snakes, which have a voracious appetite for flies (flycatchers don't, by the way; they prefer wasps and bees). Perhaps I will get the cat interested, as a sporting proposition. Meanwhile I plan to get a fresh beer and sit back with my feet up and a tightly rolled newspaper nearby. Such are the consolations of the ecological frame of mind.

BIBLIOGRAPHY

Dethier, V. G. *The Hungry Fly.* Cambridge, MA: Harvard University Press, 1976.

Greenberg, B. *Flies and Disease,* Vol. 2. Princeton, NJ: Princeton University Press, 1973.

Nachtigall, W. *Insects in Flight.* New York: McGraw-Hill, 1992.

Oldroyd, H. *The Natural History of Flies.* New York: Norton, 1964.

West, L. S. *The Housefly: Its Natural History, Medical Importance, and Control.* Ithaca, NY: Comstock Publishing, 1951.

[1] Human feces, used especially for fertilizing the soil.

[2] Remember that you must die (Latin); a memento mori is a reminder of mortality.

STUDY QUESTIONS

1. How and why were flies used as a treatment for baldness?

2. In "Why Did God Make Flies?", Conniff provides abundant detail not only about the anatomy and physiology of a housefly but also about its history with humans. What type of information does Conniff provide about the human-housefly connection? What is the purpose of this information within his essay?

3. Although it contains many facts and even some actual scientific data, Conniff's essay does not read like a traditional research paper. In what ways does the author use NARRATION and DESCRIPTION to weave an intriguing tale and create a DOMINANT IMPRESSION? Where in the essay does he reveal his personal experience with his subject? How do these more personal sections add to the rest of the essay?

4. How does Conniff write about something as ordinary as the housefly in such an extraordinary way? How does he present the information so that it is memorable and interesting? Examine paragraphs 23–28. How does Conniff present and SYNTHESIZE information to present a SUMMARY of the "hysteria against flies"?

5. *For Writing.* What might we learn from Conniff's essay about making seemingly mundane topics intriguing? Consider the ways that Conniff invites his AUDIENCE to wonder alongside him or how he presents information in a memorable way. Think about your own essays. Find a section of one that might be dry or possibly boring to your readers, and consider what you might do to make it more exciting. Following Conniff's lead, rewrite this section so that your reader has a stronger sense of what makes the topic interesting overall or of why you in particular find it intriguing.

DAVID DOBBS { *A Depression Switch?*

DAVID DOBBS (b. 1958) is a journalist who writes about science, medicine, and culture. His articles have been published in the *New York Times Magazine, Slate, Audubon,* and *Scientific American Mind,* where he is a contributing editor. Dobbs has also written several books: *The Northern Forest,* with Richard Ober (1995), *The Great Gulf: Fishermen, Scientists, and the Struggle to Revive the World's Greatest Fishery* (2000), and *Reef Madness* (2005).

The following essay, originally published in the *New York Times,* was featured in *The Best American Science Writing 2007.* In it, the author tells the story of a healthy woman who suddenly falls ill with severe depression. Dobbs analyzes the way a doctor applies a scientific discovery to alleviate the woman's illness through experimental brain surgery. As you read, take note of how Dobbs presents the step-by-step process of the procedure to the reader.

DEANNA COLE-BENJAMIN NEVER FIGURED to be a test case for a radical new brain surgery for depression. Her youth contained no traumas; her adult life, as she describes it, was blessed. At 22 she joined Gary Benjamin, a career financial officer in the Canadian Army, in a marriage that brought her happiness and, in the 1990s, three children. They lived in a comfortable house in Kingston, a pleasant university town on Lake Ontario's north shore, and Deanna, a public-health nurse, loved her work. But in the last months of 2000, apropos of nothing—no life changes, no losses—she slid into a depression of extraordinary depth and duration.

"It began with a feeling of not really feeling as connected to things as usual," she told me one evening at the family's dining-room table.

"Then it was like this wall fell around me. I felt sadder and sadder and then just numb."

Her doctor prescribed progressively stronger antidepressants, but they scarcely touched her. A couple of weeks before Christmas, she stopped going to work. The simplest acts—deciding what to wear, making breakfast—required immense will. Then one day, alone in the house after Gary had taken the kids to school and gone to work, she felt so desperate to escape her pain that she drove to her doctor's office and told him she didn't think she could go on anymore.

"He took one look," she told me later, "and said that he wanted me to stay right there in the office. Then he called Gary, and Gary came to the office, and he told us he wanted Gary to take me straight to the hospital."

They drove to the Providence Continuing Care Center's mental-health hospital, still known locally as the Kingston Psychiatric Hospital, or K.P.H., its name when it was built in the 1950s. "It's a dingy, archaic place," Deanna said, "typical of older mental hospitals." There, in the locked ward that also contained psychotic patients, she would spend the next 10 months straight and about 85 percent of the three years after that. Her depression would prove resistant to every class of antidepressant, numerous combinations of antidepressants and anti-anxiety drugs, intensive psychotherapy, and about a hundred sessions of electroconvulsive therapy. Patients who have failed that many treatments usually don't emerge from their depressions.

Finally, in the spring of 2004, Deanna's psychiatrist at the hospital, Dr. Gebrehiwot Abraham, received a fax from a University of Toronto research team asking if he had an appropriate candidate for a clinical trial of a new, experimental surgery for treatment-resistant depression. The operation borrowed a procedure called deep brain stimulation, or D.B.S., which is used to treat Parkinson's.[1] It involves planting electrodes in a region near the center of the brain called Area 25 and sending in a steady stream of low voltage from a pacemaker in the chest. One of the study's leaders, Dr. Helen Mayberg, a neurologist, had detected in depressed patients what she suspected was a crucial

[1] A degenerative disorder of the central nervous system.

dysfunction in Area 25's activity. She hypothesized that the electrodes might modulate the area and ease the depression.

The procedure, Dr. Abraham told Deanna and Gary, had worked safely in thousands of Parkinson's patients. But it would carry some risk of neural complications (it was, after all, brain surgery), it would be uncomfortable and it might not work.

"We were in tears," said Deanna, who is now 41. "We felt we'd tried everything and nothing worked. But we talked about it and decided, 'Well, what have we got to lose?'"

What she hoped to lose, of course, was her depression. But depression, which 5 to 10 percent of Americans suffer in any given year and about 15 percent will suffer in their lifetimes, can be hard to lose. Drugs, as shown in a comprehensive study released last month by the National Institute of Mental Health, are effective in only half of patients with major depression. Psychotherapy does no better. For those people who are not helped by therapy or drugs, electroconvulsive therapy, or ECT, can bring relief. But few of those cures are complete. These therapies usually ease rather than cure depression while sometimes bringing side effects like insomnia or memory loss, and their potency often proves fleeting; as many as half to two-thirds of those successfully treated relapse within two years. Neither neuroscientists nor psychiatrists can say exactly what depression is. Neurologically and psychologically, what Hippocrates called the "black bile" and Susan Sontag "melancholy minus its charms" presents an almost impossibly complicated puzzle.[2]

The expectations for the Toronto team's D.B.S. study were accordingly modest. When I later asked Mayberg's collaborator Dr. Andres Lozano, the neurosurgeon who performed the operations, what he had expected, he replied, "Nothing."

As it turned out, 8 of the 12 patients he operated on, including Deanna, felt their depressions lift while suffering minimal side effects—an incredible rate of effectiveness in patients so immovably depressed. Nor did they just vaguely recover. Their scores on the Hamilton

10

[2]Hippocrates (c. 460–c. 370 BCE), ancient Greek physician revered as "the Father of Medicine"; Susan Sontag (1933–2004), American novelist, essayist, and cultural critic.

depression scale, a standard used to measure the severity of depression, fell from the soul-deadening high 20s to the single digits—essentially normal. They've re-engaged their families, resumed jobs and friendships, started businesses, taken up hobbies old and new, replanted dying gardens. They've regained the resilience that distinguishes the healthy from the depressed.

These results brought a marvelous surprise to both the patients and the doctors involved—and nervous anticipation about whether their luck will hold. Though a few of the patients are more than two years out from the surgery, none completely trust their cure. No one can tell them for sure that it will last, and they worry. The study doctors and the wider medical community, meanwhile, are guarded about whether D.B.S. will prove so effective in larger trials. "I can't emphasize enough that we need a large, randomized study to confirm this as a treatment," says Valerie Voon, a University of Toronto psychiatrist who was with the team for the first six patients and who is now a research fellow at the National Institutes of Health.

Those caveats notwithstanding, many scientists following the trial say they believe it will change how psychiatrists define and treat mood disorders. Mayberg, who speaks of a "paradigm shift," notes that she developed the trial to evaluate not a treatment but a hypothesis. In that sense the trial succeeded. Mayberg's focus on Area 25 tests the emerging "network" model of mood disorders, a new way of looking at psychiatric conditions that isn't restricted by the neurochemical model of mood that has dominated over the past quarter century or so. Rather, it incorporates neurochemistry into the concept of the brain as a circuit board or wiring diagram. The network model carries profound implications for research and, ultimately, treatment. The Prozac revolution showed everyone that tweaking neurochemistry can dampen and sometimes extinguish depression—but only through a generalized approach, hitting the entire brain. ("Carpet-bombing," one neuroscientist calls it.) And the 50 percent success rate of antidepressant drugs suggests that they aren't hitting depression's central mechanism. The network approach, on the other hand, focuses on specific nodes, pathways and gateways that might be approached with various treatments—electrical, surgical or pharmacological. This small trial appears to confirm this model so emphatically that it's already changing the neuropsychiatric view of the brain and the direction of research.

"People often ask me about the significance of small first studies like this," says Dr. Thomas Insel, who as director of the National Institute of Mental Health enjoys an unparalleled view of the discipline. "I usually tell them: 'Don't bother. We don't know enough.' But this is different. Here we know enough to say this is something significant. I really do believe this is the beginning of a new way of understanding depression."

When she started her research in the late 1980's, Helen Mayberg, too, 15 looked at neurochemistry. "That's where biological psychiatry was then," she told me. "It was about the brain as a bowl of soup. You whip up a chemical, add it and stir. An alchemist's point of view. But I soon realized I wanted to find out where things were changing."

Lively, smart and quick-witted, Mayberg talks of brain science with contagious excitement. She possesses just the kind of presence someone having a hole drilled in his head would welcome—authoritative but warm. Mayberg originally considered becoming a psychiatrist, but she didn't like the discipline's resistance at the time (it was the 1970s) to neurological explanations of mood. So she became a behavioral neurologist, doing a residency at Columbia University and then moving to Johns Hopkins.

Setting aside the bowl-of-soup model did not mean deciding that neurochemicals weren't important. Rather it meant deciding that neurochemistry, and particularly the chemistry dictating how individual neurons communicate with one another, was probably driven by traffic between different brain areas, and that identifying the patterns in that traffic might yield new understanding. (Or, using another metaphor, if the brain is an orchestra, then the neurochemical approach focuses on how well individual players listen and respond to the players adjacent to them; the network approach, like a conductor, focuses on how the orchestra's sections—strings, winds, brass, etc.— coordinate and balance volume and tone. When both are working well, you've got music.)

Imaging tools for tracking these relationships, like PET scans and later functional magnetic resonance imagery,[3] were just maturing as Mayberg pursued her work. Neuroscientists were soon using these tools to help identify networks involved in mental processes ranging from distinguishing facial expressions to experiencing alarm or pleasure. Each of these networks engages different brain areas in different combinations. The areas active in recognizing a fearful expression, for instance, won't match those for recalling old memories, though some areas might overlap. Defining the network involved in any given process requires figuring out not just which parts are involved but also which parts are most vital and how one affects another.

By the 1990s, Mayberg was trying to define the network that goes awry in depression. She and other researchers soon established that depression involved abnormal patterns of activity in a network that includes limbic areas (a cluster of evolutionarily older brain areas around the top of the brain stem), which control basic emotions and drives like fear, lust, and hunger, and the newer cortex and subcortex responsible for thought, memory, motivation and reward.

Several researchers were working on this. But Mayberg, and, separately, Dr. Wayne Drevets, then at Washington University and now at the N.I.M.H., increasingly homed in on Area 25, which seemed crucial in both its behavior and its position in this network. They found that Area 25 was smaller in most depressed patients; that it lighted up in every form of depression and also in nondepressed people who intentionally pondered sad things; that it dimmed when depression was successfully treated; and that it was heavily wired to brain areas modulating fear, learning, memory, sleep, libido, motivation, reward and other functions that went fritzy in the depressed. It seemed to be a sort of junction box, in short, whose malfunction might be "necessary and sufficient," as Mayberg put it, to turn the world dim. Maybe it could provide a switch that would brighten the dark.

To work the switch, Mayberg needed a knife. In 1999 she moved from the University of Texas at San Antonio to the University of

20

---

[3]Positron emission tomography (PET) is a nuclear medicine imaging technique; magnetic resonance imagery is better known by its acronym, MRI.

Toronto, where she met Lozano, who had become expert at using deep brain stimulation for treating Parkinson's, the neurological affliction that causes tremors and rigidity as well as cognitive and emotional declines. By the time he and Mayberg met, he'd slipped electrodes into the brains of almost 300 patients.

Depression is more elusive than Parkinson's. But approaching Area 25 with D.B.S. allowed the researchers to use a known tool. Neurosurgeons found as early as the 1950s that they could treat Parkinson's by destroying a small portion of the hyperactive globus pallidus, a brain area that is crucial to movement. The treatment illustrated one of the brain's many oddities: some areas can cause more trouble when they are excessively active than when they have no activity at all. In the early 1990s, surgeons increasingly began to use D.B.S. to quiet the globus pallidus by sending it steady, rapid pulses of low voltage. Patients' tremors would instantly ease or cease; their rigidity and uncontrollable body movements would fade over a week or two. Killing the current revived the symptoms. Surgeons have now implanted D.B.S. electrodes in some 30,000 Parkinson's patients worldwide. The procedure is not a cure-all. It helps some patients less than others, does little to alleviate Parkinson's cognitive and emotional decay and occasionally creates complications including infection, bleeding and memory loss. Its biggest problem may be its success. So many medical centers now do it that some do it badly or on poorly qualified patients. But done well, it usually works.

Mayberg knew all this from the literature and learned more in conversations with Lozano. She grew increasingly convinced that applying D.B.S. to Area 25 might control depression.

"So one day," she told me, "I went to Lozano and said: 'I want to turn off Area 25. Can we put a stimulator there and see if that does it?' And he goes, 'Why not?' "

Occasionally, Deanna felt good enough to go home. This feeling 25 seldom lasted more than a few days. "You could tell she was getting bad again when she couldn't sleep," Gary said. "That was the red flag. She'd be around the house all night, watching TV, up worried, cleaning. Then she'd get worse each day. Her eyes got that sunken look. Those were the scariest times, when she was getting like that and I would drop the kids at school and go to work and know she was home alone."

During the bad periods, which was much of the time, Deanna thought about suicide almost constantly. Through the windows of the locked ward she could see Lake Ontario, cold and immense. While she was there, one patient managed to reach the lake, beyond the parking lot and a grove of trees, and drown himself. Deanna thought obsessively of doing the same.

"I imagined that all the time," she said. "That I would walk out there and walk into the lake and that would be it."

As the months and years passed and all treatments failed, it began to feel as if there were only one way out.

"It started to seem like, this is not going to stop," Gary said. "This is our life now. There were times I thought that it was going to end"—he looked across the table at Deanna—"only when you committed suicide."

"The worst part for me," Deanna said, "was not being able to feel anything for my children. To hug them, to have them hug me, and feel nothing. That was devastating. An awful, awful place to be."

The D.B.S. operation involves an intrusion that is delicate but brutal. The patients are kept awake so they can describe any changes, and the only drug administered is a local anesthetic. The surgical team shaves much of the patient's head and attaches to the skull, with four screws drilled through skin into bone, the stereotactic frame that will hold the head steady against the operating table and serve as a navigational aid. Mounting the frame takes only about ten minutes. But because it involves driving screws into the skull ("You can't truly feel it," as one patient said, "but you can hear it and see it and smell it"), and because it leaves you with a steel frame around the head, many patients find this the most distressing part of the whole business.

Gary found the frame more than he could take. He kissed his wife and went elsewhere, hoping she wouldn't be a vegetable when he next saw her. Then Deanna was rolled to an M.R.I. machine, where scans would be taken; the scans would help guide Lozano in placing the electrodes.

During the hour or so while the computer processed the scans, Deanna chatted with Mayberg. The day before, she told Mayberg, on video, that what she most wanted was to hold her children and feel it.

When the scans were ready, she went to the operating room. She was placed on a table, which was tilted back like a La-Z-Boy. Lozano and his team bolted the stereotactic frame to the table, as it was described to me later. There was some scrubbing on her head, some chitchat among the surgical team, much fiddling with sterile drapes and instruments. Then Lozano fit a half-inch burred bit into a drill, turned it on and started drilling. He drilled right into the top of Deanna's skull, which brought a rattling sensation and a sound like that made by an air wrench removing the lugs off a car's wheel. Then he did it again.

Now Lozano threaded a guide tube—"It's a straight shot," he said 35 later, "really quite easy"—down between crevices and seams to one side of Area 25, which is in two small lobes at the midline of the brain. He slid the first electrode and its lead down the tube, then repeated this for the other side. All this took nearly two hours. After he double-checked his locations, he wired the leads to a pacemaker and gave Mayberg a nod. They could turn it on anytime now.

Mayberg had squeezed into a spot at Deanna's side sometime before. She had told Deanna that if anything felt different, she should say so. Mayberg wasn't going to tell her when the device was activated. "Don't try to decide what's important," Mayberg told her. "If your nose itches, I want to know." Now and then the two would chat. But so far Deanna hadn't said much.

"So we turn it on," Mayberg told me later, "and all of a sudden she says to me, 'It's very strange,' she says, 'I know you've been with me in the operating room this whole time. I know you care about me. But it's not that. I don't know what you just did. But I'm looking at you, and it's like I just feel suddenly more connected to you.' "

Mayberg, stunned, signaled with her hand to the others, out of Deanna's view, to turn the stimulator off.

"And they turn it off," Mayberg said, "and she goes: 'God, it's just so odd. You just went away again. I guess it wasn't really anything.' "

"It was subtle like a brick," Mayberg told me. "There's no reason for 40 her to say that. Zero. And all through those tapes I have of her, every time she's in the clinic beforehand, she always talks about this disconnect, this closeness and sense of affiliation she misses, that was so agonizingly painful for her to lose. And there it was. It was back in an instant."

Deanna later described it in similar terms. "It was literally like a switch being turned on that had been held down for years," she said. "All of a sudden they hit the spot, and I feel so calm and so peaceful. It was overwhelming to be able to process emotion on somebody's face. I'd been numb to that for so long."

It worked that way for other patients too. For those for whom it worked, the first surges of mood and sensation were peculiar to their natures. Patient 4, for instance, was fond of taking walks, and she had previously told Mayberg that she knew she was getting ill when whole landscapes turned dim, as if "half the pixels went dark." Her first comment when the stimulator went on was to ask what they'd done to the lights, for everything seemed much brighter. Patient 5, an elite bicycle racer before his depression, told me that a pulling that he had long felt in his legs and gut, "as if death were pulling me downward," had instantly ceased. Patient 1, who in predepression days was an avid gardener, amazed the operating room by announcing that she suddenly felt as if she were walking through a field of wildflowers. Two days after going home, she put a scarf over her shaved, stitched head, found her tools and went out to reclaim her long-neglected gardens.

Not all was light and flowers. On a purely biological level, the improvement made by D.B.S. sometimes amplified the side effects of the high doses of medication the patients had been taking. Doctors don't quite understand this phenomenon, but they see it happen in other instances too; it is as if the patient, deadened, is again made sensate. Deanna broke out in hives and felt nauseated; her hands shook. These symptoms eased when she (as several of the patients have done) reduced her meds—slowly, so as not to introduce new variables. She now takes standard doses of Effexor, an antidepressant, and Seroquel, an anti-psychotic drug.

The cure also brought challenges at home. As with other disabilities, any partner turned caretaker gets used to calling the shots, and rearranging power, dependencies and expectations after a sudden recovery can prove hard. One patient, the cyclist, faced this challenge starkly, for he had started a relationship and married while he was depressed. "Frankly," he told me, "I'm not sure we've quite finished working this out." All the patients have benefited from coordinated assistance from psychiatrists, social workers and occupational therapists who try to smooth the transition.

"That help is crucial," says Mayberg, who is now a professor of psy- 45 chiatry and neurology at Emory University in Atlanta. "We're just fixing the circuit. The patient's life still needs work. It's like fixing a knee. They need that high-quality physical and supportive therapy afterward if they're really going to move around again."

This transition is not back to a former self and family but to a new one. Gary Benjamin says he sees similar things in military families. "These soldiers get sent away for six months, they come back and all they want to do is return to their old home. But their old home isn't there, because everybody's changed. It takes some tough rearranging sometimes."

For a change so profound, these seem acceptable adjustments. And the treatment so far seems remarkably free of side effects. No one has suffered significant neural complications, probably because, unlike ECT, which sends 70 to 150 volts through the entire brain, these electrodes deliver only about 4 volts to an area about the size of a pea.

But what will happen when larger groups are treated? The team is continuing to operate on depressed patients, with a goal of 20. And would the successes stay high and the side effects low in a large, placebo-controlled trial? Neither Mayberg nor any of the other collaborators cares to guess. Other treatments have started this well and fizzled. For instance, vagus nerve stimulation, which sends a low current to the brain via a major nerve with connections to various brain areas, appeared to help about half of the patients in a small, initial, uncontrolled trial, but failed its only placebo-controlled trial. (In a controversial move, the Food and Drug Administration overruled its own reviewers and approved the device as a depression treatment anyway.)

"What if you do a hundred patients," I asked Mayberg one day, "and they do no better than placebo?"

"I suppose that's possible," she said. But she doesn't think that will 50 be the case. The several authorities I talked to agree that the high success rate so far, along with the soundness of the theoretical base and D.B.S.'s track record with Parkinson's, suggests that this isn't just a lucky run.

"This just makes so much sense," says Dr. Antonio Damasio, director of the University of Southern California's Brain and Creativity Institute and a renowned neurologist, "and the weight of the results is so sizable. I would be surprised if they had no results with a larger body of patients."

On the other hand, even if it works, no one sees this becoming the new Prozac. The procedure costs too much (around $40,000) to use on anyone who hasn't tried everything else. The appropriate candidates for D.B.S. probably number in the thousands, not the millions. Perhaps the most sensible worry is that if the thing works, doctors might use it too freely, as they tend to do with successful new treatments; witness the problematic boom in D.B.S. for Parkinson's.

In the end, the procedure's greatest clinical value may lie in inspiring less-intrusive ways of tweaking key nodes—localized delivery of drug or gene therapies, or other means still to come. Such possibilities probably lie at least a decade away.

Regardless of how it pans out in the clinic, Mayberg and Lozano's D.B.S. study is already changing how neuroscientists and psychiatrists think about depression. One possibility, for instance, is that refining the networks that go awry in depression may reveal neurological subtypes of depression that can be diagnosed and treated differently. For example, Mayberg has already found that patients who respond well to Prozac usually show a change in their brain scans only a week after they start medication—even though they don't feel a difference for 3 to 10 weeks (a long and sometimes dangerous wait). She's done preliminary work suggesting she might be able to identify such Prozac-friendly patients before they even start the drug. If she or others can replicate and elaborate on this diagnostic ability, doctors might be able to characterize a patient's depression and choose a best-odds therapy—Prozac for one patient, talk therapy for a second, both for a third—at the very beginning of treatment, saving weeks or months of trial and error.

The network model—which some scientists also call a "systems" model—also offers an organizing principle for research. Andreas Meyer-Lindenberg, a researcher with the N.I.M.H., points out that research on depression has so far followed clues left by drugs that were found to be effective only by chance. "We'd find a drug that helped depression, figure out how it works, and make hypotheses from that about how the brain works," he says. The effectiveness of selective serotonin reuptake inhibitors (S.S.R.I.'s) like Prozac, for instance, inspired piles of research showing that mood regulation depends heavily on the availability of the neurotransmitters serotonin. (Neurotransmitters are chemicals that help carry messages across the spaces between neurons; S.S.R.I.'s treat depression by making more serotonin available in those spaces.)

This focus on neurotransmitters is the "bowl of soup" approach that Mayberg speaks of, and it has formed the bulk of depression research for more than two decades. Defining the networks the neurotransmitters move within, however—and in particular identifying Area 25 as a key gateway within the depression network—will let researchers bring their neurochemical knowledge to bear on specific targets.

"With this D.B.S. work," Meyer-Lindenberg says, "they have characterized in detail a system"—or network—"underlying a major disorder. It's not a simplistic thing where you're saying it's all about this one area and you inject a current and everything's fine. It's a very complicated system. But this D.B.S. work shows us that amid this complicated system there is a place of overlap, a common denominator"—Area 25—"that's a very attractive treatment target." Here, Meyer-Lindenberg says, researchers can try to apply the knowledge they've gained about neurochemistry and genetics. The network theory presents a framework around which to apply these perspectives.

Meyer-Lindenberg's own work shows the power of this approach. Last June he published a study on the serotonin transporter gene, or sert gene, which helps determine serotonin availability. Other research had shown that people with the "short" version of the sert gene run more depression risk. Meyer-Lindenberg found a way to identify how various brain areas were affected by having that short version. Then he took 112 patients, half with the long version and half with the short, scanned their brains and asked the computer to find areas that scanned differently in the two groups. The area showing the most difference was Area 25. Along with redirecting research, the quieting of Area 25 may also change our conception of depression from a condition in which something is lacking—self-esteem, resilience, optimism, energy, serotonin, you name it—to one in which an active agent makes a person sick.

"Most people think of depression as a deficit state," Mayberg says. "You're low, you're negative. But in fact, talk to a depressed person, and you have this bizarre combination of numbness and what William James called 'an active anguish.' 'A sort of psychical neuralgia,' he said, 'wholly unknown to healthy life.' You're numb but you hurt. You can't think, but you are in pain. Now, how does your psyche hurt? What a weird choice of words. But it's not an arbitrary choice. It's there. These people are feeling a particular, indescribable kind of pain."

This anguish, Mayberg suggests, is the manifestation of a neural circuit run amok. For doctors, establishing this should focus research and care. For those of us who've never known depression, recognizing it may help us see depression not as a dead absence but as a live affliction. We might even stop indulging the romantic notion of depression as intrinsic to one's identity. For this notion, too, was tested by Mayberg's experiment. When a steady, 4-volt thrum calmed these patients' anguish, they did not lose their identities. They regained them, feeling again the engagements with the world that most define them: flowers for the gardener, lightness for the cyclist, and, for Deanna, a long-missed connection to others.

When Deanna, Gary and I finally finished talking, they insisted on driving me to my hotel. Halfway through town, Gary pulled off the main road, drove up a long, sinuous driveway and parked in a lot facing a dark, rambling building.

"This is the hospital," Gary said. "You see where Deanna stayed."

In the winter dark, the secure ward, off to the left, was easily discerned. It was a low wing, the only one with a few lights still on inside. Outside, bright flood lamps illuminated an exercise yard ringed by twenty-foot-tall cyclone fencing topped with razor wire.

"And there's the lake," Gary said, motioning behind us. Through trees I could make out its blackness.

We sat several minutes, but no one said much.   65

"Well," Gary said, putting the minivan in gear. "We'd better get home."

STUDY QUESTIONS

1. Why was Deanna Cole-Benjamin an ideal candidate for experimental brain surgery? Why might deep brain stimulation in Area 25 alleviate depression?

2. Explain the PROCESS that Dr. Helen Mayberg and her colleague, Dr. Andres Lozano, followed when designing this surgical treatment for depression. In ANALYZING their process, what does Dobbs, the author, focus on? Why?

3. Consider the METAPHOR that Dobbs introduces: depression is a switch that can be flipped on or off. How does adopting this metaphor change the way doctors and patients think about depression?

4. *For Writing.* RESEARCH established treatments for depression and write an essay in which you discuss how this new procedure COMPARES to its predecessors. How has this operation transformed the way doctors think about and treat depression? Consider both its advantages and its disadvantages.

RICHARD P. FEYNMAN { *It's as Simple as One, Two, Three . . .*

RICHARD P. FEYNMAN (1918–1988), over the course of a varied and illustrious career, taught at Cornell University and the California Institute of Technology, helped develop the atomic bomb, and took part in the investigation of the space shuttle *Challenger* disaster of 1986. Feynman earned his BS from the Massachusetts Institute of Technology in 1939 and his PhD in theoretical physics from Princeton University in 1942. In 1965 he received the Nobel Prize for his work in theoretical physics. Feynman was always eager to bring physics into popular culture, writing for a general audience with both humor and clarity; his books include *Surely You're Joking, Mr. Feynman!* (1985) and *What Do You Care What Other People Think?* (1988).

"It's as Simple as One, Two, Three . . ." is both an entertaining narrative about one of Feynman's many side projects and an analysis of the scientific method as it can be applied to the simple act of counting to sixty. As you read, think about Feynman's ethos: from his tone and the stories he tells about himself, what kind of person do you think he is? How does your perception of him affect how you read his essay?

WHEN I WAS A KID growing up in Far Rockaway,[1] I had a friend named Bernie Walker. We both had "labs" at home, and we would do various "experiments." One time, we were discussing something—we must have been eleven or twelve at the time—and I said, "But thinking is nothing but talking to yourself inside."

---

[1]A town on Long Island, New York.

"Oh yeah?" Bernie said. "Do you know the crazy shape of the crankshaft in a car?"

"Yeah, what of it?"

"Good. Now, tell me: how did you describe it when you were talking to yourself?"

So I learned from Bernie that thought can be visual as well as verbal.   5

Later on, in college, I became interested in dreams. I wondered how things could look so real, just as if light were hitting the retina of the eye, while the eyes are closed: are the nerve cells on the retina actually being stimulated in some other way—by the brain itself, perhaps—or does the brain have a "judgment department" that gets slopped up during dreaming? I never got satisfactory answers to such questions from psychology, even though I became very interested in how the brain works. Instead, there was all this business about interpreting dreams, and so on.

When I was in graduate school at Princeton a kind of dumb psychology paper came out that stirred up a lot of discussion. The author had decided that the thing controlling the "time sense" in the brain is a chemical reaction involving iron. I thought to myself, "Now, how the hell could he figure that?"

Well, the way he did it was, his wife had a chronic fever which went up and down a lot. Somehow he got the idea to test her sense of time. He had her count seconds to herself (without looking at a clock), and checked how long it took her to count up to 60. He had her counting—the poor woman—all during the day: when her fever went up, he found she counted quicker; when her fever went down, she counted slower. Therefore, he thought, the thing that governed the "time sense" in the brain must be running faster when she's got fever than when she hasn't got fever.

Being a very "scientific" guy, the psychologist knew that the rate of a chemical reaction varies with the surrounding temperature by a certain formula that depends on the energy of the reaction. He measured the differences in speed of his wife's counting, and determined how much the temperature changed the speed. Then he tried to find a chemical reaction whose rates varied with temperature in the same amounts as his wife's counting did. He found that iron reactions fit the pattern best. So he deduced that his wife's sense of time was governed by a chemical reaction in her body involving iron.

Well, it all seemed like a lot of baloney to me—there were so many 10
things that could go wrong in his long chain of reasoning. But it *was* an
interesting question: what *does* determine the "time sense"? When
you're trying to count at an even rate, what does that rate depend on?
And what could you do to yourself to change it?

I decided to investigate. I started by counting seconds—without
looking at a clock, of course—up to 60 in a slow, steady rhythm: 1, 2,
3, 4, 5. . . . When I got to 60, only 48 seconds had gone by, but that
didn't bother me: the problem was not to count for exactly one minute,
but to count at a standard rate. The next time I counted to 60, 49 seconds had passed. The next time, 48. Then 47, 48, 49, 48, 48. . . . So I
found I could count at a pretty standard rate.

Now, if I just sat there, without counting, and waited until I thought
a minute had gone by, it was very irregular—complete variations. So I
found it's very poor to estimate a minute by sheer guessing. But by
counting, I could get very accurate.

Now that I knew I could count at a standard rate, the next question
was—what affects the rate?

Maybe it has something to do with the heart rate. So I began to run
up and down the stairs, up and down, to get my heart beating fast.
Then I'd run into my room, throw myself down on the bed, and count
up to 60.

I also tried running up and down the stairs and counting to myself 15
while I was running up and down.

The other guys saw me running up and down the stairs, and
laughed. "What are you doing?"

I couldn't answer them—which made me realize I couldn't talk
while I was counting to myself—and kept right on running up and
down the stairs, looking like an idiot.

(The guys at the graduate college were used to me looking like an
idiot. On another occasion, for example, a guy came into my room—I
had forgotten to lock the door during the "experiment"—and found
me in a chair wearing my heavy sheepskin coat, leaning out of the
wide-open window in the dead of winter, holding a pot in one hand
and stirring with the other. "Don't bother me! Don't bother me!" I
said. I was stirring Jell-O and watching it closely: I had gotten curious

as to whether Jell-O would coagulate in the cold if you kept it moving all the time.)

Anyway, after trying every combination of running up and down the stairs and lying on the bed, surprise! The heart rate had no effect. And since I got very hot running up and down the stairs, I figured temperature had nothing to do with it either (although I must have known that your temperature doesn't really go up when you exercise). In fact, I couldn't find anything that affected my rate of counting.

Running up and down stairs got pretty boring, so I started counting while I did things I had to do anyway. For instance, when I put out the laundry, I had to fill out a form saying how many shirts I had, how many pants, and so on. I found I could write down "3" in front of "pants" or "4" in front of "shirts," but I couldn't count my socks. There were too many of them: I'm already using my "counting machine"—36, 37, 38—and here are all these socks in front of me—39, 40, 41. . . . How do I count the socks?

I found I could arrange them in geometrical patterns—like a square, for example: a pair of socks in this corner, a pair in that one; a pair over here, and a pair over there—eight socks.

I continued this game of counting by patterns, and found I could count the lines in a newspaper article by grouping the lines into patterns of 3, 3, 3, and 1 to get 10; then 3 of those patterns, 3 of those patterns, 3 of those patterns, and 1 of those patterns made 100. I went right down the newspaper like that. After I had finished counting up to 60, I knew where I was in the patterns and could say, "I'm up to 60, and there are 113 lines." I found that I could even *read* the articles while I counted to 60, and it didn't affect the rate! In fact, I could do anything while counting to myself—except talk out loud, of course.

What about typing—copying words out of a book? I found that I could do that, too, but here my time was affected. I was excited: finally, I've found something that appears to affect my counting rate! I investigated it more.

I would go along, typing the simple words rather fast, counting to myself 19, 20, 21, typing along, counting 27, 28, 29, typing along, until—What the hell is that word?—Oh, yeah—and then continue counting 30, 31, 32, and so on. When I'd get to 60, I'd be late.

After some introspection and further observation, I realized what 25
must have happened: I would interrupt my counting when I got to a
difficult word that "needed more brains," so to speak. My counting
rate wasn't slowing down; rather, the counting itself was being held up
temporarily from time to time. Counting to 60 had become so automatic that I didn't even notice the interruptions at first.

The next morning, over breakfast, I reported the results of all these
experiments to the other guys at the table. I told them all the things I
could do while counting to myself, and said the only thing I absolutely
could not do while counting to myself was talk.

One of the guys, a fella named John Tukey, said, "I don't believe you
can read, and I don't see why you can't talk. I'll bet you I can talk while
counting to myself, and I'll bet you you can't read."

So I gave a demonstration: they gave me a book and I read it for a
while, counting to myself. When I reached 60 I said, "Now!"—48 seconds, my regular time. Then I told them what I had read.

Tukey was amazed. After we checked him a few times to see what his
regular time was, he started talking: "Mary had a little lamb; I can say
anything I want to, it doesn't make any difference; I don't know what's
bothering you"—blah, blah, blah, and finally, "Okay!" He hit his time
right on the nose! I couldn't believe it!

We talked about it a while, and we discovered something. It turned 30
out that Tukey was counting in a different way: he was visualizing a
tape with numbers on it going by. He would say, "Mary had a little
lamb," and he would *watch* it! Well, now it was clear: he's "looking" at
his tape going by, so he can't read, and I'm "talking" to myself when
I'm counting, so I can't speak!

After that discovery, I tried to figure out a way of reading out loud
while counting—something neither of us could do. I figured I'd have
to use a part of my brain that wouldn't interfere with the seeing or
speaking departments, so I decided to use my fingers, since that
involved the sense of touch.

I soon succeeded in counting with my fingers and reading out loud.
But I wanted the whole process to be mental, and not rely on any phys-
ical activity. So I tried to imagine the feeling of my fingers moving while
I was reading out loud.

I never succeeded. I figured that was because I hadn't practiced enough, but it might be impossible: I've never met anybody who can do it.

By that experience Tukey and I discovered that what goes on in different people's heads when they *think* they're doing the same thing—something as simple as *counting*—is different for different people. And we discovered that you can externally and objectively test how the brain works: you don't have to ask a person how he counts and rely on his own observations of himself; instead, you observe what he can and can't do while he counts. The test is absolute. There's no way to beat it; no way to fake it.

It's natural to explain an idea in terms of what you already have in your head. Concepts are piled on top of each other: this idea is taught in terms of that idea, and that idea is taught in terms of another idea, which comes from counting, which can be so different for different people!

I often think about that, especially when I'm teaching some esoteric technique such as integrating Bessel functions.[2] When I see equations, I see the letters in colors—I don't know why. As I'm talking, I see vague pictures of Bessel functions from Jahnke and Emde's book,[3] with light-tan j's, slightly violet-bluish n's, and dark brown x's flying around. And I wonder what the hell it must look like to the students.

---

[2] In differential calculus, equations systematized by the mathematician Friedrich Bessel (1774–1846).

[3] That is, the *Tables of Functions with Formulae and Curves*, first published in 1909.

STUDY QUESTIONS

1. What prompts Feynman to investigate how long it takes him to count to sixty? How does he test factors that might affect the rate of his counting? What do his tests reveal?

2. In this informal ANALYSIS of scientific investigation, Feynman attempts to determine whether there is a CAUSE-AND-EFFECT relationship between certain activities and the ability to count at a constant rate. How does he make this story both engaging and scientific? What does John Tukey add to the NARRATIVE and to the experiment itself?

3. *For Writing.* Choose an everyday phenomenon that intrigues you and design a PROCESS that will enable you to investigate it. In a PROPOSAL, describe the phenomenon and explain what questions it raises, suggest one or more hypotheses that might answer those questions, and then discuss how your planned process will test your hypotheses. What do you expect this investigation to achieve?

ROB FISHMAN {

*The Generation
of Generation Q*

ROB FISHMAN (b. 1986) graduated from Cornell University in 2007. While
a student there he joined the *Cornell Daily Sun*, the university's independent newspaper, as a staff writer and weekly columnist. Upon graduating, he
entered the Journalism School at Columbia University in New York City,
and he is a research assistant at the Peter G. Peterson Foundation, an organization dedicated to increasing political and personal fiscal responsibility.

In this *Daily Sun* editorial from 2007, Fishman argues that if his generation of college-age Americans is indeed "quiet," as *New York Times* columnist Thomas Friedman argued when he dubbed them "Generation Q,"
it's because technology has made them complacent: instant replay resolves
a dispute during a sporting event; Google instantly provides the forgotten
lyrics to a song. Using examples ranging from commonplaces like these to
significant moments in recent history, Fishman redefines "Generation Q"
by showing how they are all too ready to defer to technology. Do you
recognize your own behavior in his examples?

LAST WEEK, THOMAS FRIEDMAN[1] DUBBED us "Generation Q"—the
Quiet Americans, so plugged in (and tuned out) that our idealism stops
at the computer monitor. With so much interconnectedness among the
Facebook-YouTube-MySpace cohort, and so much wrong in the world,
Friedman wonders why our generation looks so complacent.

The twentysomethings fire back that their technological moving
and shaking is being mistaken for indolence; as a recent *Sun* editorial

---

[1] *New York Times* columnist and author (b. 1953).

"The Generation of Generation Q" by Rob Fishman from *The Cornell Daily Sun*, October
15, 2007. Used by permission of *The Cornell Daily Sun*.

argued, activism has "transformed from sensationalized 1960s tear-gas rallies to online petitions and Internet discussion boards."

Yet for Friedman—and, I suspect, many among the Baby Boomers and the "Greatest Generation"—we come off as apologists, hiding our apathy behind a high tech façade: "Martin Luther King and Bobby Kennedy didn't change the world by asking people to join their Facebook crusades or to download their platforms," Friedman chides us nostalgically.

In truth, we are complacent—and if you look around, for good reason.

For my generation, technology *has* had a distinctively quieting 5 effect. In nearly every walk of life, technological advancements have instilled this generation with a deep sense of inevitability that encourages us to look inward. In a sense, Friedman has it backwards: we don't lazily hide behind technology, so much as technology inspires us to stay quiet.

Take sports. In an edge-of-your seat final quarter between the Dallas Cowboys and the Buffalo Bills last week, a few of the thrills came from great catches and kicks, to be sure, but the real drama resulted from technicalities—from an instant replay review of a twenty-yard pass and from a split-second time out that voided a field goal kick that made the victory "one of the most implausible in the Cowboys' illustrious history," according to an ESPN recap of the game.

It's strange, watching these hippo-sized linemen beating the hell out of each other . . . all until a flag drops, at which point they respectfully defer to a high-definition replay.

Much the same in other sports: as the *Daily Scotsman* noted when FIFA[2] sanctioned a trial run for a soccer ball that "beeps" when it crosses the goal line, football fans can't quibble with technology that "ensure[s] justice and eradicate[s] controversy."

For sports fans and players alike, technology has obviated the important human element of competition. The exciting disputes are no longer about "bad" or "close" calls, but about close-up high-definition simu-

---

[2]The Fédération Internationale de Football Association, the international governing body for association football (professional soccer).

lacra of the plays in question; as controversy is eradicated, sports fans are, for lack of a better option, quiet.

Consider a seminal American experience for my generation: the 10 O. J. Simpson trial. In an adversarial procedure that (we now know) failed to capture the truth (if he did it, of course), the determining factor was DNA evidence, which, according to a *New York Times* article at that time, was not challenged by the defense at all on the basis of its "validity as a science."

Though the DNA evidence may not have been "clear or convincing to a jury of non-scientists," according to the *Times* article, it was ultimately presented as indisputable fact. Where Clarence Darrow drew on philosophy, religion and, yes, science to defend Leopold and Loeb in the "Trial of the Century," Johnnie Cochran's famous catchphrase was "if it doesn't fit, you must acquit."[3] Like the instant replay, DNA evidence isn't up for debate, it's a foregone conclusion.

Perhaps the most glaring example was the 2000 presidential election, when the Supreme Court upheld the voting tabulations accrued by the disputed ballots in Florida to hand the election to George W. Bush. The Court, while lamenting the "unfortunate number of ballots which [were] not punched in a clean, complete way" in *Bush v. Gore* (2000), ruled that the technology of the day would have to suffice, and that it could not read into the intent of voters—even if half a chad was clearly punched.[4]

What's dangerous in these cases is not the technology itself—for surely, we applaud fairness in sports, exonerations based on DNA evidence, and new digital voting platforms—but the excesses and unintended consequences of these innovations.

[3]The courtroom words of defense attorney Johnny Cochran (1937–2005), addressing the jury in the 1995 murder trial of O. J. Simpson after Simpson was unable to squeeze his hand into a glove found at the crime scene. *Clarence Darrow*: American lawyer (1857–1938), famed for representing thrill killers Nathan Freudenthal Leopold Jr. and Richard A. Loeb in criminal proceedings dubbed "the Trial of the Century" in 1924.

[4]In a ruling that determined the outcome of the 2000 presidential election, the U.S. Supreme Court declined to overrule Florida election officials and the Florida Supreme Court after supporters of Democratic Party candidate Al Gore argued that faulty vote-tabulating machinery had tainted the Florida vote count. (A "chad" is the tiny piece of paper displaced when a hole is punched in a computer card; such cards were used as ballots in Florida in the 2000 election.)

Thus, dinner-table disputes end as quickly as one can BlackBerry the answer; road-side directions are relics of history thanks to GPS technology; and those impossible-to-understand song lyrics no longer require funny substitutions because you can Google them straightaway. Because information is so readily accessible, technology has made us close-minded, more attuned to what's for lunch than what's on the news (though, like CNN.com, menupages.com is a mere click away).

The direst consequences of a technocracy are the stuff of entertainment: the Orwellian[5] justice system in the blockbuster hit *Minority Report* and the simulated boxing match which precedes the actual fight in *Rocky Balboa* being two prominent examples of technology meting out results before the parties have spoken. When Tom Cruise or ESPN can anticipate outcomes before events, deliberation loses meaning. 15

Is it any wonder that Generation Q, which saw the guilty O. J. vindicated by DNA evidence and the calamitous Bush crowned by faulty ballots, appears so apathetic?

Faced with the most bitter and divisive of conflicts, our societal "referees" regularly defer to technological precepts of justice over human concepts of fairness. With the world on fire, Generation Q isn't questioning the lies of WMDs in Iraq[6] or global climate change—no, we're keeping our mouths shut and burying ourselves further in our computers.

---

[5]An allusion to George Orwell's 1949 novel *Nineteen Eighty-Four,* depicting life under an oppressive totalitarian government.

[6]U.S. President George W. Bush famously cited the presence in Iraq of forbidden WMDs—weapons of mass destruction—as justification for the American invasion of 2003. Such weapons were never found.

STUDY QUESTIONS

1. Why did columnist Thomas Friedman call today's college-age Americans "Generation Q?" How does technology have what Fishman calls "unintended consequences?"

2. How does Fishman DEFINE Generation Q through its behavior? Consider the examples that Fishman uses to support his ARGUMENT. How effective are they? How might they appeal to a college AUDIENCE?

3. *For Writing.* Drawing on your own experience, write an essay in which you either defend or critique—or both defend *and* critique—Fishman's argument about how Generation Q relies on technology.

STEPHEN JAY GOULD {

Sex, Drugs, Disasters, and the

Extinction of Dinosaurs

Steven Jay Gould (1941–2002) was born in New York City; he earned his undergraduate degree at Antioch College in Ohio and his PhD at Columbia University. For thirty-five years Gould was a professor at Harvard University. However, he is best known for his ability to explain complex scientific topics in ways that make them accessible to a general audience, often by writing articles in popular magazines and by advising (and often appearing in) television programs like PBS's *NOVA*. He collected his columns from the magazine *Natural History* into several book-length collections, including *Hen's Teeth and Horse's Toes* (1983), *The Flamingo's Smile* (1985), and *Bully for Brontosaurus* (1991). The recipient of dozens of honorary degrees, Gould was a finalist for the Pulitzer Prize for his book *Wonderful Life: The Burgess Shale and the Nature of History* (1989).

The following essay, originally published in *Discover Magazine* in 1984, presents three potential hypotheses for the extinction of the dinosaurs and analyzes each for its scientific value. As you read, think about how the essay is organized and how Gould incorporates humor into a serious discussion. How might these qualities contribute to Gould's reputation as a writer who excels at presenting scientific topics to a general audience?

SCIENCE, IN ITS MOST FUNDAMENTAL definition, is a fruitful mode of inquiry, not a list of enticing conclusions. The conclusions are the consequence, not the essence. My greatest unhappiness with most popular presentations of science concerns their failure to separate fascinating claims from the methods that scientists use to establish the facts of nature. Journalists, and the public, thrive on controversial and stunning statements. But science is, basically, a way of knowing—in P. B. Medawar's apt words, "the art of the soluble." If the growing corps of popular science writers would focus on *how* scientists develop and defend those fascinating claims, they would make their greatest possible contribution to public understanding.

Consider three ideas, proposed in perfect seriousness to account for that greatest of all titillating puzzles—the extinction of dinosaurs. These three notions invoke the primarily fascinating themes of our culture—sex, drugs, and violence—and I want to show why two of them rank as silly speculation, and why the other represents science at its grandest and most useful.

Science works with testable hypotheses. If, after much compilation and scrutiny of data, new information continues to affirm a hypothesis, we may accept it provisionally and gain confidence as further evidence mounts. We can never be completely sure that a hypothesis is right, though we may be able to show with confidence that it is wrong. The best scientific hypotheses are also generous and expansive: they suggest extensions and implications that enlighten related, and even far distant, subjects. Simply consider how the idea of evolution has influenced virtually every intellectual field.

Useless speculation, on the other hand, is restrictive. It generates no testable hypothesis, proposes no way to obtain potentially refuting evidence. Please note that I am not speaking of truth or falsity. The speculation may well be true; still, if it provides, in principle, no material for affirmation or rejection, we can make nothing of it. It must simply stand forever as an intriguing idea. Useless speculation turns in on itself and leads nowhere; good science reaches out. But, enough preaching. Let's move on to dinosaurs, and the three proposed causes of their extinction.

1. Sex: Testes function only in a narrow range of temperature (those of mammals hang externally in a scrotal sac because they need to be cooler than the body). A worldwide rise in temperature at the close of the Cretaceous period caused the testes of dinosaurs to stop functioning and led to their extinction by sterilization of males.

2. Drugs: Angiosperms (flowering plants) first evolved toward the end of the dinosaurs' reign. Many of these plants contain psychoactive

agents, avoided by mammals today because of their bitter taste. Dinosaurs had neither means to taste the bitterness, nor livers effective enough to detoxify the substances. They died of massive overdoses.

3. Disasters: A huge asteroid struck the earth some 65 million years ago, lofting a cloud of dust into the sky and blocking sunlight, thereby suppressing photosynthesis and so drastically lowering world temperatures that dinosaurs and hosts of other creatures became extinct.

Before analyzing these three tantalizing statements, we must establish a basic ground rule often violated in proposals for the dinosaurs' demise. *There is no separate problem of the extinction of dinosaurs.* Too often we divorce specific events from their wider contexts and systems of cause and effect. The fundamental fact of dinosaur extinction is that it coincided with the demise of many other groups across a wide range of habitats, from terrestrial to marine.

The history of life has been punctuated by brief episodes of mass extinction. A recent analysis by University of Chicago paleontologists Jack Sepkoski and Dave Raup, based on the best and most exhaustive tabulation of data ever assembled, shows clearly that five episodes of mass dying stand well above the "background" extinctions of normal times. The Cretaceous debacle, occurring 65 million years ago and separating the Mesozoic and Cenozoic eras of our geological time scale, ranks prominently among the five. Nearly all the marine plankton (single-celled floating creatures) died suddenly, at least in geological terms; among marine invertebrates, close to 15 percent of all families perished, including many previously dominant groups, especially the ammonites (relatives of squids in coiled shells). On land, the dinosaurs disappeared after more than 100 million years of unchallenged domination.

In this context, speculations limited to dinosaurs alone ignore the 10 larger phenomenon. We need a coordinated explanation for a system of events that includes the extinction of dinosaurs as one component. Thus it makes little sense, though it may fuel our desire to view mammals as inevitable inheritors of the earth, to guess that dinosaurs died because small mammals ate their eggs (a perennial untestable speculation). It seems most unlikely that some disaster peculiar to dinosaurs befell these massive beasts—and that the debacle happened to strike just when one of history's five great dyings had enveloped the earth for completely different reasons.

The testicular theory, an old favorite from the 1940s, had its root in an interesting and thoroughly respectable study of temperature tolerances in the American alligator, published in the staid *Bulletin of the American Museum of Natural History* in 1946 by three experts on living and fossil reptiles—E. H. Colbert, my own first teacher in paleontology, R. B. Cowles, and C. M. Bogert.

The first sentence of their summary reveals a purpose beyond alligators: "This report describes an attempt to infer the reactions of extinct reptiles, especially the dinosaurs, to high temperatures as based upon reactions observed in the modern alligator." They studied, by rectal thermometry, the body temperatures of alligators under changing conditions of heating and cooling. (Well, let's face it, you wouldn't want to try sticking a thermometer under a 'gator's tongue.) The predictions under test go way back to an old theory first stated by Galileo in the 1630s—the unequal scaling of surfaces and volumes. As an animal, or any object, grows (provided its shape doesn't change), surface areas must increase more slowly than volumes—since surfaces get larger as length squared, volumes much more rapidly, as length cubed. Therefore, small animals have high ratios of surface to volume, while large animals cover themselves with relatively little surface.

Among cold-blooded animals lacking any physiological mechanism for keeping their temperatures constant, small creatures have a hell of a time keeping warm—because they lose so much heat through their relatively large surfaces. On the other hand, large animals, with their relatively small surfaces, may lose heat so slowly that, once warm, they may maintain effectively constant temperatures against ordinary fluctuations of climate. (In fact, the resolution of the "hot-blooded dinosaur" controversy of a few years back may simply be that, while large dinosaurs possessed no physiological mechanism for constant temperature, and so were not warm-blooded in the technical sense, their size and relatively small surface area kept them warm.)

Colbert, Cowles, and Bogert compared the warming rates of small and large alligators. As predicted, the small fellows heated up (and cooled down) more quickly. When exposed to a warm sun, a tiny

50-gram (1.76-ounce) alligator heated up one degree Celsius every minute and a half, while a large alligator, 260 times bigger at 13,000 grams (28.7 pounds), took seven and a half minutes to gain a degree. Extrapolating up to an adult ten-ton dinosaur, they concluded that a one-degree rise in body temperature would take 86 hours. If large animals absorb heat so slowly (through their relatively small surfaces), they will also be unable to shed any excess heat gained when temperatures rise above a favorable level.

The authors then guessed that large dinosaurs lived at or near their 15 optimum temperatures; Cowles suggested that a rise in global temperatures just before the Cretaceous extinction caused the dinosaurs to heat up beyond their optimal tolerance—and, being so large, they couldn't shed the unwanted heat. (In a most unusual statement for a scientific paper, Colbert and Bogert explicitly disavowed this speculative extension of their empirical work on alligators.) Cowles conceded that this excess heat probably wasn't enough to kill or even to enervate the great beasts, but since testes often function only within a narrow range of temperature, he proposed that this global rise might have sterilized all the males, causing extinction by natural contraception.

The overdose theory has recently been supported by UCLA psychiatrist Ronald K. Siegel. Siegel has observed, he claims, more than 2,000 animals that can give themselves various drugs—from a swig of alcohol to massive doses of the big H.[1] Elephants will swill the equivalent of twenty beers at a time, but do not like alcohol in concentrations greater than 7 per cent. In a silly bit of anthropocentric speculation, Siegel states that "elephants drink, perhaps, to forget . . . the anxiety produced by shrinking rangeland and the competition for food."

Since fertile imaginations can apply almost any hot idea to the extinction of dinosaurs, Siegel found a way. Flowering plants did not evolve until late in the dinosaurs' reign. These plants also produced an array of aromatic, amino-acid-based alkaloids—the major group of psychoactive agents. Most mammals are "smart" enough to avoid these potential poisons. The alkaloids simply don't taste good (they are

[1]Slang term for heroin.

bitter), and in any case we mammals have livers happily supplied with the capacity to detoxify them. But, Siegel speculates, perhaps dinosaurs could neither taste the bitterness nor detoxify the substances once ingested. Speaking of their extinction, he recently told members of the American Psychological Association: "I'm not suggesting that all dinosaurs OD'd on plant drugs, but it certainly was a factor." He also argued that death by overdose may help explain why so many dinosaur fossils are found in contorted positions. (Do not go gentle into that good night.)[2]

Extraterrestrial catastrophes have long pedigrees in the popular literature of extinction, but the subject exploded again after a long lull three years ago when the father-son, physicist-geologist team of Luis and Walter Alvarez proposed that an asteroid, about six miles in diameter, struck the earth 65 million years ago. Most asteroids circle the sun in an orbit between Mars and Jupiter but some, the so-called Apollo objects, take a more eccentric route, actually crossing the earth's orbit in their path around the sun. The chance of a collision at any crossing is minuscule, but the number of Apollo objects and the immensity of geological time virtually guarantee that impacts will occur once in a great while.

The force of such a collision would be immense, greater by far than the megatonnage of all the world's nuclear weapons. In trying to reconstruct a scenario that would explain the simultaneous dying of dinosaurs on land and so many creatures in the sea, the Alvarezes proposed that a gigantic dust cloud, generated by particles blown aloft in the impact, would so darken the earth that photosynthesis would cease and temperatures drop precipitously. (Rage, rage against the dying of the light.)[3] The single-celled photosynthetic oceanic plankton, with life cycles measured in weeks, would perish outright, but land plants might survive through the dormancy of their seeds (land plants were not much affected by the Cretaceous extinction, and any adequate the-

---

[2]Repeated line (and title) of a poem by Welsh poet Dylan Thomas (1914–53).

[3]Another repeating line in Thomas's poem.

ory must account for the curious pattern of differential survival). Dinosaurs would die by starvation and freezing; small, warm-blooded mammals, with more modest requirements for food and better regulation of body temperature, would squeak through.

All three theories, testicular malfunction, psychoactive overdosing, 20 and asteroidal zapping, grab our attention mightily. As pure statements, they rank about equally high on any hit parade of primal fascination. Yet one represents expansive science, the others restrictive and untestable speculation.

How could we possibly decide whether the hypothesis of testicular frying is right or wrong? We would have to know things that the fossil record cannot provide. What temperatures were optimal for dinosaurs? Could the beasts avoid the absorption of excess heat by staying in the shade, or in caves? At what temperatures did their testicles cease to function? Were late Cretaceous climates ever warm enough to drive the internal temperatures of dinosaurs close to this ceiling? Testicles simply don't fossilize, and how could we infer their temperature tolerances even if they did? In short, Cowles's hypothesis is simply an intriguing speculation leading nowhere. The most damning statement against it appeared right in the conclusion of Colbert, Cowles, and Bogert's paper, when they admitted: "It is difficult to advance any definite arguments against this hypothesis." My statement may seem paradoxical—isn't a hypothesis really good if you can't devise any arguments against it? Quite the contrary. It is simply untestable and unusable.

Siegel's overdosing has even less going for it. At least Cowles extrapolated his conclusion from some good data on alligators. And he didn't completely violate the primary guideline of explaining dinosaur extinction in the context of a general mass dying—for rise in temperature could be the root cause of a general catastrophe, zapping dinosaurs by testicular malfunction and different groups for other reasons. But Siegel's speculation cannot touch the extinction of ammonites or oceanic plankton (diatoms make their own food with good sweet sunlight; they don't OD on the chemicals of terrestrial plants). It is simply a gratuitous, attention-grabbing guess. It cannot be tested, for how can we know what dinosaurs tasted and what their livers could do?

The hypothesis doesn't even make any sense in its own context. Angiosperms were in full flower tens of millions of years before dinosaurs went the way of all flesh. Why did it take so long? As for the pains of a chemical death recorded in contortions of fossils, I regret to say (or rather I'm pleased to note for the dinosaurs' sake) that Siegel's knowledge of geology must be a bit deficient: muscles contract after death and geological strata rise and fall with motions of the earth's crust after burial—more than enough reason to distort a fossil's pristine appearance.

The asteroid story, on the other hand, has a basis in evidence. It can be tested, extended, refined and, if wrong, disproved. The Alvarezes did not just construct an arresting guess for public consumption. They proposed their hypothesis after laborious geochemical studies with Frank Asaro and Helen Michel had revealed a massive increase of iridium in rocks deposited right at the time of extinction. Iridium, a rare metal of the platinum group, is virtually absent from indigenous rocks of the earth's crust; most of our iridium comes from extraterrestrial objects that hit the earth.

The Alvarez hypothesis bore immediate fruit. Based originally on 25 evidence found in rocks at two sites in Europe, it led geochemists throughout the world to examine other sediments of the same age. They found abnormally high amounts of iridium everywhere—from continental rocks of the western United States to deep sea cores from the South Atlantic.

Cowles proposed his testicular hypothesis in the mid-1940s. Where has it gone since then? Absolutely nowhere, because scientists can do nothing with it. It merely stands as a curious appendage to a solid study of alligators. Siegel's overdose scenario will also win a few press notices and fade into oblivion. The Alvarezes' asteroid falls into a different category altogether, and much of the popular commentary has missed this essential distinction by focusing on the impact and its attendant results, and forgetting what is really important to a scientist—the iridium. If you talk just about asteroids, dust, and darkness, you simply tell stories no better and no more entertaining than fried testicles or terminal trips. It is the iridium—the source of testable evidence—that counts and forges the crucial distinction between speculation and science.

The proof, to twist a phrase, lies in the doing. In thirty-five years, Cowles's hypothesis led to no further advances toward our understanding of dinosaurian extinction. In three years, the Alvarez hypothesis has spawned hundreds of studies, a major conference, and attendant publications. Geologists are fired up. They are looking for iridium at all other extinction boundaries and, by the way, have not (with one exception) found any marked increases—thus proving that a good hypothesis also shows its worth by failing to work in other situations. Every week exposes a new wrinkle in the scientific press. In November a group of Yale scientists supported the hypothesis by finding a "cosmic signature" for isotopes of osmium in Cretaceous boundary rocks (a ratio of isotopes found in extraterrestrial material but not in crustal rocks produced on earth). Then, in December, chemists from the University of Maryland cast some doubt by reporting that volcanic eruptions of Kilauea on Hawaii had belched forth unexpectedly high levels of iridium; perhaps an extraterrestrial source need not be sought.

My point is simply this: whatever the eventual outcome (I suspect it will be positive), the Alvarez hypothesis is exciting, fruitful science because it generates tests, provides us with things to do, and expands outward. We are having fun, battling back and forth, moving toward a resolution, and extending the hypothesis beyond its original scope.

As just one example of the unexpected, distant cross-fertilization that good science engenders, the Alvarez hypothesis made a major contribution to a theme that has riveted public attention in the past few months—so-called nuclear winter. In a speech delivered in April 1982, Luis Alvarez calculated the energy that a six-mile asteroid would release on impact. He compared such an explosion with a full nuclear exchange and implied that all-out atomic war might unleash similar consequences.

This theme of impact leading to massive dust clouds and falling temperatures was an important factor in the decision of Carl Sagan and a group of colleagues to model the climatic consequences of nuclear holocaust. We have, of course, long known that a full nuclear exchange could kill half of humanity outright and cannot be deemed acceptable 30 on any grounds. But some of us still had lurking in our minds the hope that, if we hunkered down in our shelters and lived far from military sites or cities, at least we could survive after the initial fallout dropped.

Apparently, it is not necessarily so. Full nuclear exchange would probably generate the same kind of dust cloud and darkening that may have wiped out the dinosaurs. Temperatures would drop precipitously and agriculture might become impossible. Avoidance of nuclear war is fundamentally an ethical and political problem, but we must know the factual consequences to make firm judgments. Is this not a heartening thought: a recognition of the very phenomenon that made our evolution possible by exterminating the previously dominant dinosaurs and clearing a way for the evolution of large mammals, including us, might actually help to save us from joining those magnificent beasts in contorted poses among the strata of the earth.

STUDY QUESTIONS

1. Gould explores three possible explanations for the extinction of the dinosaurs. Which one of these does he think is best, and why?

2. What CRITERIA does Gould use to EVALUATE each of the three hypotheses? What other criteria might he have used? How would changing the criteria change the outcome of his evaluation? What makes for "good science," according to Gould?

3. Gould's writing is often praised as "accessible"—that is, he presents scientific information in a way that makes it understandable for nonscientists. The ORGANIZATION of this essay and its use of humor are two elements that help make it accessible; how is each suited for a general AUDIENCE? How would the essay have been different if it were written for an audience of scientists?

4. *For Writing.* Select a TOPIC for which there are multiple causes or explanations and do RESEARCH to uncover common ARGUMENTS for each explanation. In an essay, address a few of those causes or explanations and argue for the superiority of one of them. Be sure to DOCUMENT your sources using the CITATION style assigned.

JESSICA MITFORD ⎰ *Behind the Formaldehyde*
⎱ *Curtain*

JESSICA MITFORD (1917–1996) was born into an aristocratic English family
and moved in 1939 to the United States, where she became a naturalized
American citizen and pursued a career as an investigative reporter. A lifelong
activist, Mitford worked on behalf of pacifism and civil rights; when she and
her husband, Robert Treuhaft, a lawyer, became aware of funeral costs for
working-class families in the San Francisco Bay Area, she published *The
American Way of Death* (1963), which sold out on the day of publication.
While the work provoked queasiness in some readers and outrage in others
(mainly funeral directors), it has become a classic piece of expository prose,
anthologized in more than fifty textbooks. Mitford is the author of several
books, including *The American Way of Death Revisited* (1998).

This chapter from *The American Way of Death* presents a critical look at
the process of embalming bodies and preparing them for burial. Mitford
uses an ironically breezy tone to convey her attitude toward the way funerals
are conducted in the United States as she describes the procedures used to
embalm the fictitious "Mr. Jones." Despite her gruesome subject matter (or
perhaps, for some readers, because of it), Mitford's understated sense of
humor has made "Behind the Formaldehyde Curtain" enduringly popular.

THE DRAMA BEGINS TO UNFOLD with the arrival of the corpse at the
mortuary.

Alas, poor Yorick![1] How surprised he would be to see how his
counterpart of today is whisked off to a funeral parlor and is in short

---

[1]*Hamlet*, 5.1.171. Hamlet discovers the skull of an old friend in a graveyard.

---

order sprayed, sliced, pierced, pickled, trussed, trimmed, creamed, waxed, painted, rouged and neatly dressed—transformed from a common corpse into a Beautiful Memory Picture. This process is known in the trade as embalming and restorative art, and is so universally employed in the United States and Canada that the funeral director does it routinely, without consulting corpse or kin. He regards as eccentric those few who are hardy enough to suggest that it might be dispensed with. Yet no law requires embalming, no religious doctrine commends it, nor is it dictated by considerations of health, sanitation, or even of personal daintiness. In no part of the world but in Northern America is it widely used. The purpose of embalming is to make the corpse presentable for viewing in a suitably costly container; and here too the funeral director routinely, without first consulting the family, prepares the body for public display.

Is all this legal? The processes to which a dead body may be subjected are after all to some extent circumscribed by law. In most states, for instance, the signature of next of kin must be obtained before an autopsy may be performed, before the deceased may be cremated, before the body may be turned over to a medical school for research purposes; or such provision must be made in the decedent's will. In the case of embalming, no such permission is required nor is it ever sought. A textbook, *The Principles and Practices of Embalming*, comments on this: "There is some question regarding the legality of much that is done within the preparation room." The author points out that it would be most unusual for a responsible member of a bereaved family to instruct the mortician, in so many words, to *"embalm"* the body of a deceased relative. The very term "embalming" is so seldom used that the mortician must rely upon custom in the matter. The author concludes that unless the family specifies otherwise, the act of entrusting the body to the care of a funeral establishment carries with it an implied permission to go ahead and embalm.

Embalming is indeed a most extraordinary procedure, and one must wonder at the docility of Americans who each year pay hundreds of millions of dollars for its perpetuation, blissfully ignorant of what it is all about, what is done, how it is done. Not one in ten thousand has any idea of what actually takes place. Books on the subject are extremely hard to come by. They are not to be found in most libraries or bookshops.

In an era when huge television audiences watch surgical operations 5 in the comfort of their living rooms, when, thanks to the animated cartoon, the geography of the digestive system has become familiar territory even to the nursery school set, in a land where the satisfaction of curiosity about almost all matters is a national pastime, the secrecy surrounding embalming can, surely, hardly be attributed to the inherent gruesomeness of the subject. Custom in this regard has within this century suffered a complete reversal. In the early days of American embalming, when it was performed in the home of the deceased, it was almost mandatory for some relative to stay by the embalmer's side and witness the procedure. Today, family members who might wish to be in attendance would certainly be dissuaded by the funeral director. All others, except apprentices, are excluded by law from the preparation room.

A close look at what does actually take place may explain in large measure the undertaker's intractable reticence concerning a procedure that has become his major *raison d'être*. Is it possible he fears that public information about embalming might lead patrons to wonder if they really want this service? If the funeral men are loath to discuss the subject outside the trade, the reader may, understandably, be equally loath to go on reading at this point. For those who have the stomach for it, let us part the formaldehyde curtain. Others should skip to paragraph 20.

The body is first laid out in the undertaker's morgue—or rather, Mr. Jones is reposing in the preparation room—to be readied to bid the world farewell.

The preparation room in any of the better funeral establishments has the tiled and sterile look of a surgery, and indeed the embalmer-restorative artist who does his chores there is beginning to adopt the term "dermasurgeon" (appropriately corrupted by some mortician-writers as "demisurgeon") to describe his calling. His equipment, consisting of scalpels, scissors, augers, forceps, clamps, needles, pumps, tubes, bowls and basins, is crudely imitative of the surgeon's, as is his technique, acquired in a nine- or twelve-month post-high-school course in an embalming school. He is supplied by an advanced chemical industry with a bewildering array of fluids, sprays, pastes, oils, powders, creams, to fix or soften tissue, shrink or distend it as needed, dry it here, restore the moisture there. There are cosmetics, waxes and paints to fill and cover features, even plaster of Paris to replace entire limbs. There are ingenious aids to prop and stabilize the cadaver: a Vari-Pose Head Rest, the Edwards Arm and Hand Positioner, the Repose Block (to support the shoulders, during the embalming), and the Throop Foot Positioner, which resembles an old-fashioned stocks.

Mr. John H. Eckels, president of the Eckels College of Mortuary Science, thus describes the first part of the embalming procedure: "In the hands of a skilled practitioner, this work may be done in a comparatively short time and without mutilating the body other than by slight incision—so slight that it scarcely would cause serious inconvenience if made upon a living person. It is necessary to remove the blood, and doing this not only helps in the disinfecting, but removes the principal cause of disfigurements due to discoloration."

Another textbook discusses the all-important time element: "The 10 earlier this is done, the better, for every hour that elapses between death and embalming will add to the problems and complications encountered. . . ." Just how soon should one get going on the embalming? The author tells us, "On the basis of such scanty information made available to this profession through its rudimentary and haphazard system of technical research, we must conclude that the best results are to be obtained if the subject is embalmed before life is completely extinct—that is, before cellular death has occurred. In the average case, this would mean within an hour after somatic death." For those who feel that there is something a little rudimentary, not to say haphazard, about this advice, a comforting thought is offered by another writer. Speaking of fears entertained in early days of premature burial, he points out, "One of the effects of embalming by chemical injection, however, has been to dispel fears of live burial." How true; once the blood is removed, chances of live burial are indeed remote.

To return to Mr. Jones, the blood is drained out through the veins and replaced by embalming fluid pumped in through the arteries. As noted in *The Principles and Practices of Embalming,* "every operator has a favorite injection and drainage point—a fact which becomes a handicap only if he fails or refuses to forsake his favorites when conditions demand it." Typical favorites are the carotid artery, femoral artery, jugular vein, subclavian vein. There are various choices of embalming fluid. If Flextone is used, it will produce a "mild, flexible rigidity. The skin retains a velvety softness, the tissues are rubbery and pliable. Ideal for women and children." It may be blended with B. and G. Products Company's Lyf-Lyk tint, which is guaranteed to reproduce "nature's own skin texture . . . the velvety appearance of living tissue." Suntone comes in three separate tints: Suntan; Special Cosmetic Tint, a pink shade "especially indicated for young female subjects"; and Regular Cosmetic Tint, moderately pink.

About three to six gallons of a dyed and perfumed solution of formaldehyde, glycerin, borax, phenol, alcohol and water is soon circulating through Mr. Jones, whose mouth has been sewn together with a "needle directed upward between the upper lip and gum and brought out through the left nostril," with the corners raised slightly "for a more pleasant expression." If he should be bucktoothed, his teeth are cleaned with Bon Ami and coated with colorless nail polish. His eyes, meanwhile, are closed with flesh-tinted eye caps and eye cement.

The next step is to have at Mr. Jones with a thing called a trocar. This is a long, hollow needle attached to a tube. It is jabbed into the abdomen, poked around the entrails and chest cavity, the contents of which are pumped out and replaced with "cavity fluid." This done, and the hole in the abdomen sewn up, Mr. Jones's face is heavily creamed (to protect the skin from burns which may be caused by leakage of the chemicals), and he is covered with a sheet and left unmolested for a while. But not for long—there is more, much more, in store for him. He has been embalmed, but not yet restored, and the best time to start the restorative work is eight to ten hours after embalming, when the tissues have become firm and dry.

The object of all this attention to the corpse, it must be remembered, is to make it presentable for viewing in an attitude of healthy repose. "Our customs require the presentation of our dead in the semblance of normality . . . unmarred by the ravages of illness, disease, or mutilation," says Mr. J. Sheridan Mayer in his *Restorative Art.* This is rather a large order since few people die in the full bloom of health, unravaged by illness and unmarked by some disfigurement. The funeral industry is equal to the challenge: "In some cases the gruesome appearance of a mutilated or disease-ridden subject may be quite discouraging. The task of restoration may seem impossible and shake the confidence of the embalmer. This is the time for intestinal fortitude and determination. Once the formative work is begun and affected tissues are cleaned or removed, all doubts of success vanish. It is surprising and gratifying to discover the results which may be obtained."

The embalmer, having allowed an appropriate interval to elapse, 15 returns to the attack, but now he brings into play the skill and equipment of sculptor and cosmetician. Is a hand missing? Casting one in plaster of Paris is a simple matter. "For replacement purposes, only a cast of the back of the hand is necessary; this is within the ability of the average operator and is quite adequate." If a lip or two, a nose or an ear should be missing, the embalmer has at hand a variety of restorative waxes with which to model replacements. Pores and skin texture are simulated by stippling with a little brush, and over this cosmetics are laid on. Head off? Decapitation cases are rather routinely handled. Ragged edges are trimmed, and head joined to torso with a series of splints, wires and sutures. It is a good idea to have a little something at the neck—a scarf or high collar—when time for viewing comes. Swollen mouth? Cut out tissue as needed from inside the lips. If too much is removed, the surface contour can easily be restored by padding with cotton. Swollen necks and cheeks are reduced by removing tissue through vertical incisions made down each side of the neck. "When the deceased is casketed, the pillow will hide the suture incisions . . . as an extra precaution against leakage, the suture may be painted with liquid sealer."

The opposite condition is more likely to present itself—that of emaciation. His hypodermic syringe now loaded with massage cream, the embalmer seeks out and fills the hollowed and sunken areas by injection. In this procedure the backs of the hands and fingers and the under-chin area should not be neglected.

Positioning the lips is a problem that recurrently challenges the ingenuity of the embalmer. Closed too tightly, they tend to give a stern, even disapproving expression. Ideally, embalmers feel, the lips should give the impression of being ever so slightly parted, the upper lip protruding slightly for a more youthful appearance. This takes some engineering, however, as the lips tend to drift apart. Lip drift can sometimes be remedied by pushing one or two straight pins through the inner margin of the lower lip and then inserting them between the two front upper teeth. If Mr. Jones happens to have no teeth, the pins can just as easily be anchored in his Armstrong Face Former and Denture Replacer. Another method to maintain lip closure is to dislocate the lower jaw, which is then held in its new position by a wire run through holes which have been drilled through the upper and lower jaws at the midline. As the French are fond of saying, *il faut souffrir pour être belle.*[2]

If Mr. Jones has died of jaundice, the embalming fluid will very likely turn him green. Does this deter the embalmer? Not if he has intestinal fortitude. Masking pastes and cosmetics are heavily laid on, burial garments and casket interiors are color-correlated with particular care, and Jones is displayed beneath rose-colored lights. Friends will say, "How *well* he looks." Death by carbon monoxide, on the other hand, can be rather a good thing from the embalmer's viewpoint: "One advantage is the fact that this type of discoloration is an exaggerated form of a natural pink coloration." This is nice because the healthy glow is already present and needs but little attention.

The patching and filling completed, Mr. Jones is now shaved, washed and dressed. Cream-based cosmetic, available in pink, flesh, suntan, brunette and blond, is applied to his hands and face, his hair is shampooed and combed (and, in the case of Mrs. Jones, set), his hands manicured. For the horny-handed son of toil special care must be taken; cream should be applied to remove ingrained grime, and the nails cleaned. "If he were not in the habit of having them manicured in

---

[2]In 1963 *Mortuary Management* reports a new development: "Natural Expression Formers," an invention of Funeral Directors Research Company. "They may be used to replace one or both artificial dentures, or over natural teeth; have 'bite-indicator' lines as a closure guide . . . Natural Expression Formers also offer more control of facial expression" [Author's note]. *Il faut souffrir pour être belle:* One must suffer to be beautiful (French).

life, trimming and shaping is advised for better appearance—never questioned by kin."

Jones is now ready for casketing (this is the present participle of 20 the verb "to casket"). In this operation his right shoulder should be depressed slightly "to turn the body a bit to the right and soften the appearance of lying flat on the back." Positioning the hands is a matter of importance, and special rubber positioning blocks may be used. The hands should be cupped slightly for a more lifelike, relaxed appearance. Proper placement of the body requires a delicate sense of balance. It should lie as high as possible in the casket, yet not so high that the lid, when lowered, will hit the nose. On the other hand, we are cautioned, placing the body too low "creates the impression that the body is in a box."

Jones is next wheeled into the appointed slumber room where a few last touches may be added—his favorite pipe placed in his hand or, if he was a great reader, a book propped into position. (In the case of little Master Jones a Teddy bear may be clutched.) Here he will hold open house for a few days, visiting hours 10 A.M. to 9 P.M.

All now being in readiness, the funeral director calls a staff conference to make sure that each assistant knows his precise duties. Mr. Wilber Krieger writes: "This makes your staff feel that they are a part of the team, with a definite assignment that must be properly carried out if the whole plan is to succeed. You never heard of a football coach who failed to talk to his entire team before they go on the field. They have drilled on the plays they are to execute for hours and days, and yet the successful coach knows the importance of making even the bench-warming third-string substitute feel that he is important if the game is to be won." The winning of *this* game is predicated upon glass-smooth handling of the logistics. The funeral director has notified the pallbearers whose names were furnished by the family, has arranged for the presence of clergyman, organist, and soloist, has provided transportation for everybody, has organized and listed the flowers sent by friends. In *Psychology of Funeral Service* Mr. Edward A. Martin points out: "He may not always do as much as the family thinks he is doing, but it is his helpful guidance that they appreciate in knowing they are proceeding as they should. . . . The important thing is how well his services can be used to make the family believe they are giving unlimited expression to their own sentiment."

The religious service may be held in a church or in the chapel of the funeral home; the funeral director vastly prefers the latter arrangement, for not only is it more convenient for him but it affords him the opportunity to show off his beautiful facilities to the gathered mourners. After the clergyman has had his say, the mourners queue up to file past the casket for a last look at the deceased. The family is *never* asked whether they want an open-casket ceremony; in the absence of their instruction to the contrary, this is taken for granted. Consequently well over 90 percent of all American funerals feature the open casket—a custom unknown in other parts of the world. Foreigners are astonished by it. An English woman living in San Francisco described her reaction in a letter to the writer:

> I myself have attended only one funeral here—that of an elderly fellow worker of mine. After the service I could not understand why everyone was walking towards the coffin (sorry, I mean casket), but thought I had better follow the crowd. It shook me rigid to get there and find the casket open and poor old Oscar lying there in his brown tweed suit, wearing a suntan makeup and just the wrong shade of lipstick. If I had not been extremely fond of the old boy, I have a horrible feeling that I might have giggled. Then and there I decided that I could never face another American funeral—even dead.

The casket (which has been resting throughout the service on a Classic Beauty Ultra Metal Casket Bier) is now transferred by a hydraulically operated device called Porto-Lift to a balloon-tired, Glide Easy casket carriage which will wheel it to yet another conveyance, the Cadillac Funeral Coach. This may be lavender, cream, light green—anything but black. Interiors, of course, are color-correlated, "for the man who cannot stop short of perfection."

At graveside, the casket is lowered into the earth. This office, once the prerogative of friends of the deceased, is now performed by a patented mechanical lowering device. A "Lifetime Green" artificial grass mat is at the ready to conceal the sere earth, and overhead, to conceal the sky, is a portable Steril Chapel Tent ("resists the intense heat and humidity of summer and the terrific storms of winter . . . available in Silver Grey, Rose or Evergreen"). Now is the time for the ritual scattering of earth over the coffin, as the solemn words "earth to earth, ashes to ashes, dust to dust" are pronounced by the officiating cleric. This can today be accomplished "with a mere flick of the wrist with the Gordon Leak-Proof Earth Dispenser. No grasping of a handful of dirt, no soiled fingers. Simple, dignified, beautiful, reverent! The modern way!" The Gordon Earth Dispenser (at $5) is of nickel-plated brass construction. It is not only "attractive to the eye and long wearing"; it is also "one of the 'tools' for building better public relations" if presented as "an appropriate non-commercial gift" to the clergyman. It is shaped something like a saltshaker.

Untouched by human hand, the coffin and the earth are now united.

It is in the function of directing the participants through this maze of gadgetry that the funeral director has assigned to himself his relatively new role of "grief therapist." He has relieved the family of every detail, he has revamped the corpse to look like a living doll, he has arranged for it to nap for a few days in a slumber room, he has put on a well-oiled performance in which the concept of *death* has played no part whatsoever—unless it was inconsiderately mentioned by the clergyman who conducted the religious service. He has done everything in his power to make the funeral a real pleasure for everybody concerned. He and his team have given their all to score an upset victory over death.

STUDY QUESTIONS

1. In paragraph 6, Mitford invites the reader to "part the formaldehyde curtain." What does she mean? How is the formaldehyde curtain like the "Iron Curtain" that divided western and eastern Europe during the Cold War era?

2. Mitford writes a PROCESS essay about embalming. However, rather than simply list each step, she DESCRIBES and EXPLAINS each part of the process. Identify two steps that are fully explained and discuss your reaction to them. Does this kind of process essay help you better understand the subject? Explain.

3. Consider the TOPIC and the TONE of the article. Do you think the two are consistent? Describe the tone that Mitford uses to explain the process of embalming. Who is her intended AUDIENCE? Rewrite one or two steps using a different tone for a different audience.

4. *For Writing.* Consider a process that you are familiar with. Write a process essay that explains the steps to complete the activity. Use Mitford's essay as a model—don't just list the steps, explain the steps and DESCRIBE the equipment needed to perform the activity. Write the paper for two different audiences: one that is familiar with the process and one that is unfamiliar with it.

SCOTT RUSSELL SANDERS { *The Inheritance of Tools*

SCOTT RUSSELL SANDERS (b. 1945), born in Memphis, Tennessee, grew
up mainly in Ohio. He graduated from Brown University in 1967 and
received his PhD from Cambridge University in 1971. He has taught at
Indiana University since 1971. The author of eight novels and eleven works
of nonfiction, he has written widely on environmental issues, social justice,
and community.

In "The Inheritance of Tools," Sanders meditates on the proper use of
tools and the virtue and morality of building with one's hands, knowledge
that has been passed down through the generations of Sanders men. He
brings together past and present as he describes passing on his own knowledge to his children. By the end of his essay, Sanders has described not only
his tools and their history, but also what those tools represent—purpose,
timelessness, and love.

_____

AT JUST ABOUT THE HOUR when my father died, soon after dawn one
February morning when ice coated the windows like cataracts, I
banged my thumb with a hammer. Naturally I swore at the hammer, the
reckless thing, and in the moment of swearing I thought of what my
father would say: "If you'd try hitting the nail it would go in a whole
lot faster. Don't you know your thumb's not as hard as that hammer?"
We both were doing carpentry that day, but far apart. He was building
cupboards at my brother's place in Oklahoma; I was at home in
Indiana putting up a wall in the basement to make a bedroom for my
daughter. By the time my mother called with news of his death—the

"The Inheritance of Tools" first appeared in The North American Review; from *The
Paradise of Bombs*. Copyright © 1986 by Scott Russell Sanders. Used by permission of the
author and the author's agents, the Virginia Kidd Agency, Inc.

long-distance wires whittling her voice until it seemed too thin to bear the weight of what she had to say—my thumb was swollen. A week or so later a white scar in the shape of a crescent moon began to show above the cuticle, and month by month it rose across the pink sky of my thumbnail. It took the better part of a year for the scar to disappear, and every time I noticed it I thought of my father.

The hammer had belonged to him, and to his father before him. The three of us have used it to build houses and barns and chicken coops, to upholster chairs and crack walnuts, to make doll furniture and bookshelves and jewelry boxes. The head is scratched and pock-marked, like an old plowshare that has been working rocky fields, and it gives off the sort of dull sheen you see on fast creek water in the shade. It is a finishing hammer, about the weight of a bread loaf, too light really for framing walls, too heavy for cabinetwork, with a curved claw for pulling nails, a rounded head for pounding, a fluted neck for looks, and a hickory handle for strength.

The present handle is my third one, bought from a lumberyard in Tennessee down the road from where my brother and I were helping my father build his retirement house. I broke the previous one by try-ing to pull sixteen-penny nails out of floor joists—a foolish thing to do with a finishing hammer, as my father pointed out. "You ever hear of a crowbar?" he said. No telling how many handles he and my grandfa-ther had gone through before me. My grandfather used to cut down hickory trees on his farm, saw them into slabs, cure the planks in his hayloft, and carve handles with a drawknife. The grain in hickory is crooked and knotty, and therefore tough, hard to split, like the grain in the two men who owned this hammer before me.

After proposing marriage to a neighbor girl, my grandfather used this hammer to build a house for his bride on a stretch of river bottom in northern Mississippi. The lumber for the place, like the hickory for the handle, was cut on his own land. By the day of the wedding he had not quite finished the house, and so right after the ceremony he took his wife home and put her to work. My grandmother had worn her Sunday dress for the wedding, with a fringe of lace tacked on around the hem in honor of the occasion. She removed this lace and folded it away before going out to help my grandfather nail siding on the house.

"There she was in her good dress," he told me some fifty-odd years after that wedding day, "holding up them long pieces of clapboard while I hammered, and together we got the place covered up before dark." As the family grew to four, six, eight, and eventually thirteen, my grandfather used this hammer to enlarge his house room by room, like a chambered nautilus expanding his shell.

By and by the hammer was passed along to my father. One day he 5 was up on the roof of our pony barn nailing shingles with it, when I stepped out the kitchen door to call him for supper. Before I could yell, something about the sight of him straddling the spine of that roof and swinging the hammer caught my eye and made me hold my tongue. I was five or six years old, and the world's commonplaces were still news to me. He would pull a nail from the pouch at his wrist, bring the hammer down, and a moment later the *thunk* of the blow would reach my ears. And that is what had stopped me in my tracks and stilled my tongue, that momentary gap between seeing and hearing the blow. Instead of yelling from the kitchen door, I ran to the barn and climbed two rungs up the ladder—as far as I was allowed to go—and spoke quietly to my father. On our walk to the house he explained that sound takes time to make its way through air. Suddenly the world seemed larger, the air more dense, if sound could be held back like any ordinary traveler.

By the time I started using this hammer, at about the age when I discovered the speed of sound, it already contained houses and mysteries for me. The smooth handle was one my grandfather had made. In those days I needed both hands to swing it. My father would start a nail in a scrap of wood, and I would pound away until I bent it over.

"Looks like you got ahold of some of those rubber nails," he would tell me. "Here, let me see if I can find you some stiff ones." And he would rummage in a drawer until he came up with a fistful of more cooperative nails. "Look at the head," he would tell me. "Don't look at your hands, don't look at the hammer. Just look at the head of that nail and pretty soon you'll learn to hit it square."

Pretty soon I did learn. While he worked in the garage cutting dovetail joints for a drawer or skinning a deer or tuning an engine, I would hammer nails. I made innocent blocks of wood look like porcupines.

He did not talk much in the midst of his tools, but he kept up a nearly ceaseless humming, slipping in and out of a dozen tunes in an afternoon, often running back over the same stretch of melody again and again, as if searching for a way out. When the humming did cease, I knew he was faced with a task requiring great delicacy or concentration, and I took care not to distract him.

He kept scraps of wood in a cardboard box—the ends of two-by-fours, slabs of shelving and plywood, odd pieces of molding—and everything in it was fair game. I nailed scraps together to fashion what I called boats or houses, but the results usually bore only faint resemblance to the visions I carried in my head. I would hold up these constructions to show my father, and he would turn them over in his hands admiringly, speculating about what they might be. My cobbled-together guitars might have been alien spaceships, my barns might have been models of Aztec temples, each wooden contraption might have been anything but what I had set out to make.

Now and again I would feel the need to have a chunk of wood 10 shaped or shortened before I riddled it with nails, and I would clamp it in a vice and scrape at it with a handsaw. My father would let me lacerate the board until my arm gave out, and then he would wrap his hand around mine and help me finish the cut, showing me how to use my thumb to guide the blade, how to pull back on the saw to keep it from binding, how to let my shoulder do the work.

"Don't force it," he would say, "just drag it easy and give the teeth a chance to bite."

As the saw teeth bit down the wood released its smell, each kind with its own fragrance, oak or walnut or cherry or pine—usually pine, because it was the softest and the easiest for a child to work. No matter how weathered and gray the board, no matter how warped and cracked, inside there was this smell waiting, as of something freshly baked. I gathered every smidgen of sawdust and stored it away in coffee cans, which I kept in a drawer of the workbench. When I did not feel like hammering nails I would dump my sawdust on the concrete floor of the garage and landscape it into highways and farms and towns, running miniature cars and trucks along miniature roads. Looming as huge as a colossus, my father worked over and around me, now and again bending down to inspect my work, careful not to trample my creations. It was a landscape that smelled dizzyingly of wood. Even after a bath my skin would carry the smell, and so would my father's hair, when he lifted me for a bedtime hug.

I tell these things not only from memory but also from recent observation, because my own son now turns blocks of wood into nailed porcupines, dumps cans full of sawdust at my feet and sculpts highways on the floor. He learns how to swing a hammer from the elbow instead of the wrist, how to lay his thumb beside the blade to guide a saw, how to tap a chisel with a wooden mallet, how to mark a hole with an awl before starting a drill bit. My daughter did the same before him, and even now, on the brink of teenage aloofness, she will occasionally drag out my box of wood scraps and carpenter something. So I have seen my apprenticeship to wood and tools reenacted in each of my children, as my father saw his own apprenticeship renewed in me.

The saw I use belonged to him, as did my level and both of my squares, and all four tools had belonged to his father. The blade of the saw is the bluish color of gun barrels, and the maple handle, dark from the sweat of hands, is inscribed with curving leaf designs. The level is a shaft of walnut two feet long, edged with brass and pierced by three round windows in which air bubbles float in oil-filled tubes of glass. The middle window serves for testing whether a surface is horizontal, the others for testing whether it is plumb or vertical. My grandfather used to carry this level on the gun rack behind the seat in his pickup, and when I rode with him I would turn around to watch the bubbles dance. The larger of the two squares is called a framing square, a flat steel elbow so beat up and tarnished you can barely make out the rows of numbers that show how to figure the cuts on rafters. The smaller one is called a try square, for marking right angles, with a blued steel blade for the shank and a brass-faced block of cherry for the head.

I was taught early on that a saw is not to be used apart from a square: "If you're going to cut a piece of wood," my father insisted, "you owe it to the tree to cut it straight."

Long before studying geometry, I learned there is a mystical virtue in right angles. There is an unspoken morality in seeking the level and the plumb. A house will stand, a table will bear weight, the sides of a box will hold together only if the joints are square and the members upright. When the bubble is lined up between two marks etched in the glass tube of a level, you have aligned yourself with the forces that hold the universe together. When you miter the corners of a picture frame, each angle must be exactly forty-five degrees, as they are in the perfect triangles of Pythagoras, not a degree more or less. Otherwise the frame will hang crookedly, as if ashamed of itself and of its maker. No matter if the joints you are cutting do not show. Even if you are butting two pieces of wood together inside a cabinet, where no one except a wrecking crew will ever see them, you must take pains to insure that the ends are square and the studs are plumb.

I took pains over the wall I was building on the day my father died. Not long after that wall was finished—paneled with tongue-and-groove boards of yellow pine, the nail holes filled with putty and the wood all stained and sealed—I came close to wrecking it one afternoon when my daughter ran howling up the stairs to announce that her gerbils had escaped from their cage and were hiding in my brand-new wall. She could hear them scratching and squeaking behind her bed. Impossible! I said. How on earth could they get inside my drum-tight wall? Through the heating vent, she answered. I went downstairs, pressed my ear to the honey-colored wood, and heard the scritch scritch of tiny feet.

"What can we do?" my daughter wailed. "They'll starve to death, they'll die of thirst, they'll suffocate." "Hold on," I soothed. "I'll think of something."

While I thought and she fretted, the radio on her bedside table delivered us the headlines. Several thousand people had died in a city in India from a poisonous cloud that had leaked overnight from a chemical plant. A nuclear-powered submarine had been launched. Rioting continued in South Africa. An airplane had been hijacked in the Mediterranean. Authorities calculated that several thousand homeless people slept on the streets within sight of the Washington Monument. I felt my usual helplessness in face of all these calamities. But here was my daughter weeping because her gerbils were holed up in a wall. This calamity I could handle.

"Don't worry," I told her. "We'll set food and water by the heating 20 vent and lure them out. And if that doesn't do the trick, I'll tear the wall apart until we find them."

She stopped crying and gazed at me. "You'd really tear it apart? Just for my gerbils? The *wall*?" Astonishment slowed her down only for a second, however, before she ran to the workbench and began tugging at drawers, saying, "Let's see, what'll we need? Crowbar. Hammer. Chisels. I hope we don't have to use them—but just in case."

We didn't need the wrecking tools. I never had to assault my handsome wall, because the gerbils eventually came out to nibble at a dish of popcorn. But for several hours I studied the tongue-and-groove skin I had nailed up on the day of my father's death, considering where to begin prying. There were no gaps in that wall, no crooked joints.

I had botched a great many pieces of wood before I mastered the right angle with a saw, botched even more before I learned to miter a joint. The knowledge of these things resides in my hands and eyes and the webwork of muscles, not in the tools. There are machines for sale— powered miter boxes and radial arm saws, for instance—that will enable any casual soul to cut proper angles in boards. The skill is invested in the gadget instead of the person who uses it, and this is what distinguishes a machine from a tool. If I had to earn my keep by making furniture or building houses, I suppose I would buy powered saws and pneumatic nailers; the need for speed would drive me to it. But since I carpenter only for my own pleasure or to help neighbors or to remake the house around the ears of my family, I stick with hand tools. Most of the ones I own were given to me by my father, who also taught me how to wield them. The tools in my workbench are a double inheritance, for each hammer and level and saw is wrapped in a cloud of knowing.

All of these tools are a pleasure to look at and to hold. Merchants would never paste NEW NEW NEW! signs on them in stores. Their designs are old because they work, because they serve their purpose well. Like folksongs and aphorisms and the grainy bits of language, these tools have been pared down to essentials. I look at my claw hammer, the distillation of a hundred generations of carpenters, and consider that it holds up well beside those other classics—Greek vases, Gregorian chants, *Don Quixote,* barbed fishhooks, candles, spoons.

Knowledge of hammering stretches back to the earliest humans who squatted beside fires chipping flints. Anthropologists have a lovely name for those unworked rocks that served as the earliest hammers. "Dawn stones" they are called. Their only qualification for the work, aside from hardness, is that they fit the hand. Our ancestors used them for grinding corn, tapping awls, smashing bones. From dawn stones to this claw hammer is a great leap in time, but no great distance in design or imagination.

On that iced-over February morning when I smashed my thumb   25
with the hammer, I was down in the basement framing the wall that my daughter's gerbils would later hide in. I was thinking of my father, as I always did whenever I built anything, thinking how he would have gone about the work, hearing in memory what he would have said about the wisdom of hitting the nail instead of my thumb. I had the studs and plates nailed together all square and trim, and was lifting the wall into place when the phone rang upstairs. My wife answered, and in a moment she came to the basement door and called down softly to me. The stillness in her voice made me drop the framed wall and hurry upstairs. She told me my father was dead. Then I heard the details over the phone from my mother. Building a set of cupboards for my brother in Oklahoma, he had knocked off work early the previous afternoon because of cramps in his stomach. Early this morning, on his way into the kitchen of my brother's trailer, maybe going for a glass of water, so early that no one else was awake, he slumped down on the linoleum and his heart quit.

For several hours I paced around inside my house, upstairs and down, in and out of every room, looking for the right door to open and knowing there was no such door. My wife and children followed me and wrapped me in arms and backed away again, circling and staring as if I were on fire. Where was the door, the door, the door? I kept wondering. My smashed thumb turned purple and throbbed, making me furious. I wanted to cut it off and rush outside and scrape away the snow and hack a hole in the frozen earth and bury the shameful thing.

I went down into the basement, opened a drawer in my workbench, and stared at the ranks of chisels and knives. Oiled and sharp, as my father would have kept them, they gleamed at me like teeth. I took up a clasp knife, pried out the longest blade, and tested the edge on the hair of my forearm. A tuft came away cleanly, and I saw my father testing the sharpness of tools on his own skin, the blades of axes and knives and gouges and hoes, saw the red hair shaved off in patches from his arms and the backs of his hands. "That will cut bear," he would say. He never cut a bear with his blades, now my blades, but he cut deer, dirt, wood. I closed the knife and put it away. Then I took up the hammer and went back to work on my daughter's wall, snugging the bottom place against a chalkline on the floor, shimming the top plate against the joists overhead, plumbing the studs with my level, making sure before I drove the first nail that every line was square and true.

STUDY QUESTIONS

1. What advice did Sanders's father give him about hammering nails? What did Sanders make from the various chunks of wood his father gave him? What was Sanders's greatest achievement as a builder?

2. ANALYZE Sander's DESCRIPTION of his hammer (paragraphs 2–6). How does the hammer look, sound, and feel? How does this description contribute to Sander's overall NARRATIVE?

3. Sanders begins and ends his MEMOIR of his father by recounting what he is doing just before and just after he learns of his father's death. Why do you think he chose to frame the narrative in this way? What is the significance to this essay of using this rhetorical strategy? How does the word "frame" fit both the strategy and the subject?

4. *For Writing.* Choose a person who is special in your life, and make a list of some experiences that you have shared. Select the experience that stirs the most emotions, that best displays your relationship with this person, and that you can write about. Using DESCRIPTION, PATHOS, and any other rhetorical strategies that will give your AUDIENCE a full picture of your subject, write a memoir of this special person.

SAMUEL SCUDDER   { *Look at Your Fish: In the*
                     Laboratory with Agassiz

SAMUEL SCUDDER (1837–1911) the first North American insect paleontologist, was born in Boston, Massachusetts, and educated at both Williams College, graduating in 1857, and Harvard University, graduating in 1862. Well known for advocating firsthand observation as an indispensable part of the scientific process, Scudder published extensively—more than seven hundred articles during the course of his career. He was twice president of the Boston Society of Natural History, cofounder of the Cambridge Entomological Club's journal *Psyche*, and the first editor of the journal *Science*.

In the following selection, Scudder recounts the story of his first encounter with the famed paleontologist Louis Agassiz at Harvard University. It tells of an impatient young biology student, bored after ten minutes of looking at a dead fish, who discovers that he cannot really begin to engage in science at all until he immerses himself in the process of observation, which can take days, even months, in order to understand something. Consider how well you think you know the physical structure or the behavior of a family member, a pet, or even yourself. Do you think you might learn something new with closer, longer observations?

IT WAS MORE THAN FIFTEEN years ago that I entered the laboratory of Professor Agassiz, and told him I had enrolled my name in the scientific school as a student of natural history. He asked me a few questions about my object in coming, my antecedents generally, the mode in which I afterwards proposed to use the knowledge I might acquire, and finally, whether I wished to study any special branch. To the latter I replied that while I wished to be well grounded in all departments of zoology, I purposed to devote myself specially to insects.

"When do you wish to begin?" he asked.

"Now," I replied.

This seemed to please him, and with an energetic "Very well," he reached from a shelf a huge jar of specimens in yellow alcohol.

"Take this *fish*," said he, "and look at it; we call it a Hæmulon; by 5
and by I will ask what you have seen."

With that he left me, but in a moment returned with explicit instructions as to the care of the object entrusted to me.

"No man is fit to be a naturalist," said he, "who does not know how to take care of specimens."

I was to keep the fish before me in a tin tray, and occasionally moisten the surface with alcohol from the jar, always taking care to replace the stopper tightly. Those were not the days of ground glass stoppers, and elegantly shaped exhibition jars; all the old students will recall the huge, neckless glass bottles with their leaky, wax-besmeared corks, half eaten by insects and begrimed with cellar dust. Entomology was a cleaner science than ichthyology, but the example of the professor, who had unhesitatingly plunged to the bottom of the jar to produce the fish, was infectious; and though this alcohol had "a very ancient and fish-like smell," I really dared not show any aversion within these sacred precincts, and treated the alcohol as though it were pure water. Still I was conscious of a passing feeling of disappointment, for gazing at a fish did not commend itself to an ardent entomologist. My friends at home, too, were annoyed, when they discovered that no amount of eau de cologne would drown the perfume which haunted me like a shadow.

In ten minutes I had seen all that could be seen in that fish, and started in search of the professor, who had however left the museum; and when I returned, after lingering over some of the odd animals stored in the upper apartment, my specimen was dry all over. I dashed the fluid over the fish as if to resuscitate the beast from a fainting-fit, and looked with anxiety for a return of the normal, sloppy appearance. This little excitement over, nothing was to be done but return to a steadfast gaze at my mute companion. Half an hour passed,—an hour,—another hour; the fish began to look loathsome. I turned it over and around; looked it in the face,—ghastly; from behind, beneath, above, sideways, at a three quarters' view,—just as ghastly. I was in despair; at an early hour I concluded that lunch was necessary; so, with infinite relief, the fish was carefully replaced in the jar, and for an hour I was free.

On my return, I learned that Professor Agassiz had been at the museum, but had gone and would not return for several hours. My fellow-students were too busy to be disturbed by continued conversation. Slowly I drew forth that hideous fish, and with a feeling of desperation again looked at it. I might not use a magnifying glass; instruments of all kinds were interdicted. My two hands, my two eyes, and the fish; it seemed a most limited field. I pushed my finger down its throat to feel how sharp the teeth were. I began to count the scales in the different rows until I was convinced that that was nonsense. At last a happy thought struck me—I would draw the fish; and now with surprise I began to discover new features in the creature. Just then the professor returned.

"That is right," said he; "a pencil is one of the best of eyes. I am glad to notice, too, that you keep your specimen wet and your bottle corked."

With these encouraging words, he added,—

"Well, what is it like?"

He listened attentively to my brief rehearsal of the structure of parts whose names were still unknown to me: the fringed gill-arches and movable operculum; the pores of the head, fleshy lips, and lidless eyes; the lateral line, the spinous fins, and forked tail; the compressed and arched body. When I had finished, he waited as if expecting more, and then, with an air of disappointment,—

"You have not looked very carefully; why," he continued, more earnestly, "you haven't even seen one of the most conspicuous features of the animal, which is as plainly before your eyes as the fish itself; look again, look again!" and he left me to my misery.

I was piqued; I was mortified. Still more of that wretched fish! But now I set myself to my task with a will, and discovered one new thing after another, until I saw how just the professor's criticism had been. The afternoon passed quickly, and when, toward its close, the professor inquired,—

"Do you see it yet?"

"No," I replied, "I am certain I do not, but I see how little I saw before."

"That is next best," said he, earnestly, "but I won't hear you now; put away your fish and go home; perhaps you will be ready with a better answer in the morning. I will examine you before you look at the fish."

This was disconcerting; not only must I think of my fish all night, 20 studying, without the object before me, what this unknown but most visible feature might be; but also, without reviewing my new discoveries, I must give an exact account of them the next day. I had a bad memory; so I walked home by Charles River[1] in a distracted state, with my two perplexities.

The cordial greeting from the professor the next morning was reassuring; here was a man who seemed to be quite as anxious as I, that I should see for myself what he saw.

"Do you perhaps mean," I asked, "that the fish has symmetrical sides with paired organs?"

His thoroughly pleased, "Of course, of course!" repaid the wakeful hours of the previous night. After he had discoursed most happily and enthusiastically—as he always did—upon the importance of this point, I ventured to ask what I should do next.

"Oh, look at your fish!" he said, and left me again to my own devices. In a little more than an hour he returned and heard my new catalogue.

"That is good, that is good!" he repeated; "but that is not all; go on;" 25 and so for three long days he placed that fish before my eyes, forbidding me to look at anything else, or to use any artificial aid. "Look, look, look," was his repeated injunction.

This was the best entomological lesson I ever had,—a lesson, whose influence has extended to the details of every subsequent study; a legacy the professor has left to me, as he has left it to many others, of inestimable value, which we could not buy, with which we cannot part.

[1]Massachusetts river between Boston and Cambridge.

A year afterward, some of us were amusing ourselves with chalking outlandish beasts upon the museum blackboard. We drew prancing star-fishes; frogs in mortal combat; hydra-headed worms; stately craw-fishes, standing on their tails, bearing aloft umbrellas; and grotesque fishes with gaping mouths and staring eyes. The professor came in shortly after, and was as amused as any, at our experiments. He looked at the fishes.

"Hæmulons, every one of them," he said; "Mr. ——[2] drew them."

True; and to this day, if I attempt a fish, I can draw nothing but Hæmulons.

The fourth day, a second fish of the same group was placed beside the first, and I was bidden to point out the resemblances and differences between the two; another and another followed, until the entire family lay before me, and a whole legion of jars covered the table and surrounding shelves; the odor had become a pleasant perfume; and even now, the sight of an old, six-inch, worm-eaten cork brings fragrant memories!

The whole group of Hæmulons was thus brought in review; and, whether engaged upon the dissection of the internal organs, the preparation and examination of the bony frame-work, or the description of the various parts, Agassiz' training in the method of observing facts and their orderly arrangement was ever accompanied by the urgent exhortation not to be content with them.

"Facts are stupid things," he would say, "until brought into connection with some general law."

At the end of eight months, it was almost with reluctance that I left these friends and turned to insects; but what I had gained by this outside experience has been of greater value than years of later investigation in my favorite groups.

[2]The article originally appeared anonymously—"BY A FORMER PUPIL."

STUDY QUESTIONS

1. What is the student's initial mindset regarding lab work? How does it change? What sensory details enliven Scudder's DESCRIPTION of his first days in the laboratory?

2. What kind of PROCESS does Professor Agassiz encourage? How is this process both challenging and helpful to the student?

3. What kind of ORGANIZATION does Scudder use to present the process of learning to observe? What other organization might he have used?

4. *For Writing.* Choose something to observe—perhaps an animal, a plant, or even yourself—and spend several days looking at it carefully. Then in an essay ANALYZE your process of observation and what it yielded. What did you learn and how did you learn it?

BRAD STONE { *Web of Risks*

BRAD STONE (b. 1971) was born in Cleveland. After graduating from
Columbia University in 1993, he joined *Newsweek* magazine and worked as
the Silicon Valley correspondent for almost a decade, covering technology
and business while also writing an online column on the role of technology
in society. In 2006 Stone moved to the *New York Times* San Francisco
bureau, where he reports on Internet trends and consumer technology. He
also posts to *Bits*, the *Times* technology blog.

In "Web of Risks," originally published in *Newsweek*, Stone cautions
those who use social-networking sites to be sensible about what they post
on sites such as Facebook, which in 2006, when the article was written, was
available only to college students. Using testimony from students who have
been cited for their posts or even expelled from college, Stone explains that
while these sites may exist only online, the documents and images that are
posted on them can have real-world repercussions. His article raises serious
questions about the responsibility that students should take for their online
posts—and about the degree to which colleges can or should monitor the
online lives of their students.

CAMERON WALKER LEARNED THE HARD way that sharing information
online can have unintended consequences. In 2005, the sophomore at
Fisher College in Boston organized a student petition dedicated to getting a campus police guard fired and posted it on the popular college
social network Facebook.com. Walker wrote that the guard "loves to
antagonize students . . . and needs to be eliminated." It was a poor

choice of words. Another student informed school officials, who logged on and interpreted the comments as threatening. Though Walker claimed he was trying only to expose the guard's demeanor, he was expelled. He's now enrolled at another college and admits he made a serious mistake. "I was a naive twenty-one-year-old," he says.

Creating a page on a social-networking site is now a cherished form of self-expression at universities around the world. Students use ad-supported services like Facebook, MySpace, TagWorld and Bebo to make friends, plan their social lives, and project their personalities. The most popular site among college students is Facebook, with more than 8 million members. A student's personal Facebook page is usually a revealing, dynamic chronicle of campus life—one clearly not meant for the eyes of parents, teachers or anyone else older than twenty-five.

But adults are taking notice. Sites like Facebook are accessible to nearly anyone willing to spend the time to gain access: teachers, school administrators, even potential employers and the police. Such online services can create the illusion of privacy where none actually exists. Facebook, in particular, was designed to emphasize privacy and intimacy. Only other users at your school (with the same college e-mail domain name), and those in networks you join, can see your home page. But determined off-campus visitors can persuade a student or alumnus to help them access the student's page.

What happens when the identity you reveal to friends suddenly overwhelms the façade you present to grownups? The results can be awkward—or worse. Photos from drunken parties, recollections of sexual escapades, profanity or threats—all these indiscretions, posted online, have gotten students suspended or expelled, or harmed job prospects. In a couple of decades, a presidential candidate may be called on to answer for a college misadventure that he or she impetuously detailed in a blog entry.

Harvard student Marc Zuckerberg and a few classmates designed 5 Facebook in 2003 to facilitate contact among students. After it launched in early 2004, the service spread like the flu in a freshman dorm, first at Harvard and then to all 2,100 four-year colleges. Last year the company opened its digital doors to high schoolers. Early on, Zuckerberg left college and moved his fledgling enterprise to Silicon

Valley, raising more than $35 million in venture capital. Facebook now has 100 employees and is supported by big advertisers like Apple and MasterCard.

Facebook's founders worried about privacy. That's why it isn't one big network but a series of connected smaller ones. "We decided early on that you get better information flow and more trust if you limit access to just those around you," says Zuckerberg. Besides restricting access to a student's classmates, Facebook offers extra privacy tools. Students can limit parts of their pages, such as photos, to specific people. Still, just 17 percent of customers ever change those privacy settings.

For many students, Facebook is not only an interactive diary and yearbook, but a pervasive way to stay in touch. Mitchell Perley, an Atlanta-born student at the University of Edinburgh in Scotland, is typical. On his page there's a photo with a friend at Disneyland, mentions of his membership in such Facebook groups as the Krispy Kreme Appreciation Society and listings of his favorite musicians and films. Perhaps most important, his page is linked to the pages of 99 friends at his college and 845 back home at various U.S. schools.

But not everyone's Facebook experiences have been positive. Brad Davis was a freshman at Emory in Atlanta in 2005 when he and friends commemorated a night of drinking by posting photos of themselves in their dorm, hoisting their libations. They created a Facebook group called the Dobbs 2nd Floor Alcoholics, named after their dorm. A dorm adviser saw the photos and reported the underage imbibers. The school ordered Davis and his friends to hang anti-drinking posters on their walls, and a citation went on their records.

The consequences for Jason Johnson were more serious. He was a student at the University of the Cumberlands, a Southern Baptist school in Williamsburg, Kentucky, when he created his own MySpace page. Visitors to his page could hear a favorite song, learn his birthday or find out he was gay. But Cumberlands' student handbook states that students must lead a "Christian lifestyle," which the school president explained included a ban on homosexuality. When school officials discovered Johnson's page, he was expelled. He hired a lawyer, who got the school to rescind the expulsion and let Johnson transfer with his academic record intact.

Students' indiscriminate postings may also get them into trouble 10 when they're applying for a job or to graduate school. The postings could still be accessible online despite students' efforts to delete them. Even though companies are loath to admit it, researching candidates on social networks is becoming as easy and prevalent as entering their names into Google. Laurie Sybel, a director of career development at Vermont Technical College, had never looked at Facebook until she got a call from a big company about the internship application of a nineteen-year-old. The student was being rejected, Sybel recalls, because executives had viewed the student's Facebook page, which contained a photo of him holding a bottle of vodka. The company noted that the student was not only apparently breaking the law but demonstrating bad judgment by publishing the photo. In response, Vermont Technical, like other colleges, now integrates tips for social-network decorum into its career-guidance workshops.

Not all students want to temper their behavior. They point out that the Internet lets them express themselves and find like-minded souls. Still, adults aren't likely to stop prying any time soon. That means students who use Facebook and MySpace have a new burden. The Web may seem ephemeral, but what you casually post one night might just last a digital eternity. While social networking represents a powerful tool for today's students, they're advised to be prudent. Even if they have no plans to run for president someday.

STUDY QUESTIONS

1. How did Facebook, a popular social-networking site, begin? What, according to Stone, are some of its positive and negative aspects?

2. What is Stone's CLAIM? What REASONS and what kinds of EVIDENCE does he provide to support that claim? How effective are they?

3. What is the CAUSE-AND-EFFECT relationship between students' online postings and the unintended consequences Stone cites in the article? Have these students been treated fairly? Why or why not?

4. *For Writing.* Stone highlights numerous "privacy tools" that Facebook offers its users. But few students make use of them, and many choose to disclose personal information, images, or philosophies that Facebook does not solicit. Should students be expelled or otherwise penalized for the ideas and images that they post? In an essay, ARGUE your POSITION, being sure to support each of your points with reasons and evidence.

BARBARA TUCHMAN ⎰ *"This Is the End of the*
World": The Black Death

BARBARA TUCHMAN (1912–1989) was born in New York City and graduated from Radcliffe College with a BA in 1933. She began her journalism
career in the editorial department of the *Nation*, and she later covered the
Spanish Civil War for a London periodical. Tuchman wrote several critically
acclaimed books on historical events and periods, making history accessible
for a general audience. She won the Pulitzer Prize twice, for *The Guns of
August* (1962) and for *Stilwell and the American Experience in China,
1911–45* (1971). Tuchman also received the National Endowment for the
Humanities' highest honor in 1980, when she was selected to give the Jefferson Lecture.

In "This Is the End of the World," drawn from her book *A Distant Mirror:
The Calamitous Fourteenth Century* (1978), Tuchman traces the causes
and effects of the Black Death in medieval Europe. With careful description
and meticulously researched statistics, she brings to life the terror of this
disease. As you read, think about how Tuchman makes a vast, complicated
topic palatable for a general, nonacademic audience. How and how effectively does she reach that audience?

IN OCTOBER 1347, TWO MONTHS after the fall of Calais,[1] Genoese
trading ships put into the harbor of Messina in Sicily with dead and
dying men at the oars. The ships had come from the Black Sea port of
Caffa (now Feodosiya) in the Crimea, where the Genoese maintained a
trading post. The diseased sailors showed strange black swellings about

---

[1]Port city in northern France that had been captuared by Edward III.

the size of an egg or an apple in the armpits and groin. The swellings oozed blood and pus and were followed by spreading boils and black blotches on the skin from internal bleeding. The sick suffered severe pain and died quickly within five days of the first symptoms. As the disease spread, other symptoms of continuous fever and spitting of blood appeared instead of the swellings or buboes. These victims coughed and sweated heavily and died even more quickly, within three days or less, sometimes in twenty-four hours. In both types everything that issued from the body—breath, sweat, blood from the buboes and lungs, bloody urine, and blood-blackened excrement—smelled foul. Depression and despair accompanied the physical symptoms, and before the end "death is seen seated on the face."

The disease was bubonic plague, present in two forms: one that infected the bloodstream, causing the buboes and internal bleeding, and was spread by contact; and a second, more virulent pneumonic type that infected the lungs and was spread by respiratory infection. The presence of both at once caused the high mortality and speed of contagion. So lethal was the disease that cases were known of persons going to bed well and dying before they woke, of doctors catching the illness at a bedside and dying before the patient. So rapidly did it spread from one to another that to a French physician, Simon de Covino, it seemed as if one sick person "could infect the whole world." The malignity of the pestilence appeared more terrible because its victims knew no prevention and no remedy.

The physical suffering of the disease and its aspect of evil mystery were expressed in a strange Welsh lament which saw "death coming into our midst like black smoke, a plague which cuts off the young, a rootless phantom which has no mercy for fair countenance. Woe is me of the shilling in the armpit! It is seething, terrible . . . a head that gives pain and causes a loud cry . . . a painful angry knob. . . . Great is its seething like a burning cinder . . . a grievous thing of ashy color." Its eruption is ugly like the "seeds of black peas, broken fragments of brittle sea-coal . . . the early ornaments of black death, cinders of the peelings of the cockle weed, a mixed multitude, a black plague like halfpence, like berries. . . ."

Rumors of a terrible plague supposedly arising in China and spreading through Tartary (Central Asia) to India and Persia, Mesopotamia, Syria, Egypt, and all of Asia Minor had reached Europe in 1346. They told of a death toll so devastating that all of India was said to be depopulated, whole territories covered by dead bodies, other areas with no one left alive. As added up by Pope Clement VI at Avignon, the total of reported dead reached 23,840,000. In the absence of a concept of contagion, no serious alarm was felt in Europe until the trading ships brought their black burden of pestilence into Messina while other infected ships from the Levant carried it to Genoa and Venice.

By January 1348 it penetrated France via Marseille, and North 5 Africa via Tunis. Shipborne along coasts and navigable rivers, it spread westward from Marseille through the ports of Languedoc to Spain and northward up the Rhône to Avignon, where it arrived in March. It reached Narbonne, Montpellier, Carcassonne, and Toulouse between February and May, and at the same time in Italy spread to Rome and Florence and their hinterlands. Between June and August it reached Bordeaux, Lyon, and Paris, spread to Burgundy and Normandy, and crossed the Channel from Normandy into southern England. From Italy during the same summer it crossed the Alps into Switzerland and reached eastward to Hungary.

In a given area the plague accomplished its kill within four to six months and then faded, except in the larger cities, where, rooting into the close-quartered population, it abated during the winter, only to reappear in spring and rage for another six months.

In 1349 it resumed in Paris, spread to Picardy, Flanders, and the Low Countries, and from England to Scotland and Ireland as well as to Norway, where a ghost ship with a cargo of wool and a dead crew drifted offshore until it ran aground near Bergen. From there the plague passed into Sweden, Denmark, Prussia, Iceland, and as far as Greenland. Leaving a strange pocket of immunity in Bohemia, and Russia unattacked until 1351, it had passed from most of Europe by mid-1350. Although the mortality rate was erratic, ranging from one-fifth in some places to nine-tenths or almost total elimination in others, the overall estimate of modern demographers has settled—for the area extending from India to Iceland—around the same figure expressed in Froissart's[2] casual words: "a third of the world died." His estimate, the common one at the time, was not an inspired guess but a borrowing of St. John's figure for mortality from plague in Revelation, the favorite guide to human affairs of the Middle Ages.

A third of Europe would have meant about twenty million deaths. No one knows in truth how many died. Contemporary reports were an awed impression, not an accurate count. In crowded Avignon, it was said, four hundred died daily; seven thousand houses emptied by death were shut up; a single graveyard received eleven thousand corpses in six weeks; half the city's inhabitants reportedly died, including nine cardinals or one-third of the total, and seventy lesser prelates. Watching the endlessly passing death carts, chroniclers let normal exaggeration take wings and put the Avignon death toll at 62,000 and even at 120,000, although the city's total population was probably less than 50,000.

When graveyards filled up, bodies at Avignon were thrown into the Rhône until mass burial pits were dug for dumping the corpses. In London in such pits corpses piled up in layers until they overflowed. Everywhere reports speak of the sick dying too fast for the living to bury. Corpses were dragged out of homes and left in front of doorways. Morning light revealed new piles of bodies. In Florence the dead were gathered up by the Compagnia della Misericordia—founded in 1244 to care for the sick—whose members wore red robes and hoods masking the face except for the eyes. When their efforts failed, the dead lay putrid in the streets for days at a time. When no coffins were to be had, the bodies were laid on boards, two or three at once, to be carried to graveyards or common pits. Families dumped their own relatives into the pits, or buried them so hastily and thinly "that dogs dragged them forth and devoured their bodies."

Amid accumulating death and fear of contagion, people died without last rites and were buried without prayers, a prospect that terrified the last hours of the stricken. A bishop in England gave permission to   10

[2]Jean Froissart (c. 1337–c. 1405), medieval historian.

laymen to make confession to each other as was done by the Apostles, "or if no man is present then even to a woman," and if no priest could be found to administer extreme unction, "then faith must suffice." Clement VI found it necessary to grant remissions of sin to all who died of the plague because so many were unattended by priests. "And no bells tolled," wrote a chronicler of Siena, "and nobody wept no matter what his loss because almost everyone expected death. . . . And people said and believed, 'This is the end of the world.' "

In Paris, where the plague lasted through 1349, the reported death rate was eight hundred a day, in Pisa five hundred, in Vienna five to six hundred. The total dead in Paris numbered fifty thousand or half the population. Florence, weakened by the famine of 1347, lost three- to four-fifths of its citizens, Venice two-thirds, Hamburg and Bremen, though smaller in size, about the same proportion. Cities, as centers of transportation, were more likely to be affected than villages, although once a village was infected, its death rate was equally high. At Givry, a prosperous village in Burgundy of twelve to fifteen hundred people, the parish register records 615 deaths in the space of fourteen weeks, compared to an average of thirty deaths a year in the previous decade. In three villages of Cambridgeshire, manorial records show a death rate of 47 percent, 57 percent, and in one case 70 percent. When the last survivors, too few to carry on, moved away, a deserted village sank back into the wilderness and disappeared from the map altogether, leaving only a grass-covered ghostly outline to show where mortals once had lived.

In enclosed places such as monasteries and prisons, the infection of one person usually meant that of all, as happened in the Franciscan convents of Carcassonne and Marseille, where every inmate without exception died. Of the one hundred forty Dominicans at Montpellier only seven survived. Petrarch's[3] brother Gherardo, member of a Carthusian monastery, buried the prior and thirty-four fellow monks one by one, sometimes three a day, until he was left alone with his dog and fled to look for a place that would take him in. Watching every

---

[3]Francesco Petrarch (1304–74), Italian Renaissance poet famed for his sonnets.

comrade die, men in such places could not but wonder whether the strange peril that filled the air had not been sent to exterminate the human race. In Kilkenny, Ireland, Brother John Clyn of the Friars Minor, another monk left alone among dead men, kept a record of what had happened lest "things which should be remembered perish with time and vanish from the memory of those who come after us." Sensing "the whole world, as it were, placed within the grasp of the Evil One," and waiting for death to visit him too, he wrote, "I leave parchment to continue this work, if perchance any man survive and any of the race of Adam escape this pestilence and carry on the work which I have begun." Brother John, as noted by another hand, died of the pestilence, but he foiled oblivion.

The largest cities of Europe, with populations of about one hundred thousand, were Paris and Florence, Venice and Genoa. At the next level, with more than fifty thousand, were Ghent and Bruges in Flanders, Milan, Bologna, Rome, Naples, and Palermo, and Cologne. London hovered below fifty thousand, the only city in England except York with more than ten thousand. At the level of twenty to fifty thousand were Bordeaux, Toulouse, Montpellier, Marseille, and Lyon in France, Barcelona, Seville, and Toledo in Spain, Siena, Pisa, and other secondary cities in Italy, and the Hanseatic trading cities of the Empire. The plague raged through them all, killing anywhere from one-third to two-thirds of their inhabitants. Italy, with a total population of ten to eleven million, probably suffered the heaviest toll. Following the Florentine bankruptcies, the crop failures and workers' riots of 1346–47, the revolt of Cola di Rienzi that plunged Rome into anarchy, the plague came as the peak of successive calamities. As if the world were indeed in the grasp of the Evil One, its first appearance on the European mainland in January 1348 coincided with a fearsome earthquake that carved a path of wreckage from Naples up to Venice. Houses collapsed, church towers toppled, villages were crushed, and the destruction reached as far as Germany and Greece. Emotional response, dulled by horrors, underwent a kind of atrophy epitomized by the chronicler who wrote, "And in these days was burying without sorrowe and wedding without friendschippe."

In Siena, where more than half the inhabitants died of the plague, work was abandoned on the great cathedral, planned to be the largest in the world, and never resumed, owing to loss of workers and master masons and "the melancholy and grief" of the survivors. The cathedral's truncated transept still stands in permanent witness to the sweep of death's scythe. Agnolo di Tura, a chronicler of Siena, recorded the fear of contagion that froze every other instinct. "Father abandoned child, wife husband, one brother another," he wrote, "for this plague seemed to strike through the breath and sight. And so they died. And no one could be found to bury the dead for money or friendship. . . . And I, Agnolo di Tura, called the Fat, buried my five children with my own hands, and so did many others likewise."

There were many to echo his account of inhumanity and few to balance it, for the plague was not the kind of calamity that inspired mutual help. Its loathsomeness and deadliness did not herd people together in mutual distress, but only prompted their desire to escape each other. "Magistrates and notaries refused to come and make the wills of the dying," reported a Franciscan friar of Piazza in Sicily; what was worse, "even the priests did not come to hear their confessions." A clerk of the Archbishop of Canterbury reported the same of English priests who "turned away from the care of their benefices from fear of death." Cases of parents deserting children and children their parents were reported across Europe from Scotland to Russia. The calamity chilled the hearts of men, wrote Boccaccio[4] in his famous account of the plague in Florence that serves as introduction to the *Decameron.* "One man shunned another . . . kinsfolk held aloof, brother was forsaken by brother, oftentimes husband by wife; nay, what is more, and scarcely to be believed, fathers and mothers were found to abandon their own children to their fate, untended, unvisited as if they had been strangers." Exaggeration and literary pessimism were common in the fourteenth century, but the Pope's physician, Guy de Chauliac, was a sober, careful observer who reported the same phenomenon: "A father did not visit his son, nor the son his father. Charity was dead."

Yet not entirely. In Paris, according to the chronicler Jean de Venette, the nuns of the Hôtel Dieu or municipal hospital, "having no

15

---

[4]Giovanni Boccaccio (1313–75), Italian writer of *The Decameron,* a group of stories told by characters who have fled plague-ridden Florence.

fear of death, tended the sick with all sweetness and humility." New nuns repeatedly took the places of those who died, until the majority "many times renewed by death now rest in peace with Christ as we may piously believe."

When the plague entered northern France in July 1348, it settled first in Normandy and, checked by winter, gave Picardy a deceptive interim until the next summer. Either in mourning or warning, black flags were flown from church towers of the worst-stricken villages of Normandy. "And in that time," wrote a monk of the abbey of Fourcarment, "the mortality was so great among the people of Normandy that those of Picardy mocked them." The same unneighborly reaction was reported of the Scots, separated by a winter's immunity from the English. Delighted to hear of the disease that was scourging the "southrons," they gathered forces for an invasion, "laughing at their enemies." Before they could move, the savage mortality fell upon them too, scattering some in death and the rest in panic to spread the infection as they fled.

In Picardy in the summer of 1349 the pestilence penetrated the castle of Coucy to kill Enguerrand's[5] mother, Catherine, and her new husband. Whether her nine-year-old son escaped by chance or was perhaps living elsewhere with one of his guardians is unrecorded. In nearby Amiens, tannery workers, responding quickly to losses in the labor force, combined to bargain for higher wages. In another place villagers were seen dancing to drums and trumpets, and on being asked the reason, answered that, seeing their neighbors die day by day while their village remained immune, they believed they could keep the plague from entering "by the jollity that is in us. That is why we dance." Further north in Tournai on the border of Flanders, Gilles li Muisis, Abbot of St. Martin's, kept one of the epidemic's most vivid accounts. The passing bells rang all day and all night, he recorded, because sextons were anxious to obtain their fees while they could. Filled with the sound of mourning, the city became oppressed by fear, so that the authorities forbade the tolling of bells and the wearing of black and

[5]Enguerrand VII de Coucy (1340–97), French nobleman who serves as an organizing figure in Tuchman's book.

restricted funeral services to two mourners. The silencing of funeral bells and of criers' announcements of deaths was ordained by most cities. Siena imposed a fine on the wearing of mourning clothes by all except widows.

Flight was the chief recourse of those who could afford it or arrange it. The rich fled to their country places like Boccaccio's young patricians of Florence, who settled in a pastoral palace "removed on every side from the roads" with "wells of cool water and vaults of rare wines." The urban poor died in their burrows, "and only the stench of their bodies informed neighbors of their death." That the poor were more heavily afflicted than the rich was clearly remarked at the time, in the north as in the south. A Scottish chronicler, John of Fordun, stated flatly that the pest "attacked especially the meaner sort and common people—seldom the magnates." Simon de Covino of Montpellier made the same observation. He ascribed it to the misery and want and hard lives that made the poor more susceptible, which was half the truth. Close contact and lack of sanitation was the unrecognized other half. It was noticed too that the young died in greater proportion than the old; Simon de Covino compared the disappearance of youth to the withering of flowers in the fields.

In the countryside peasants dropped dead on the roads, in the fields, in their houses. Survivors in growing helplessness fell into apathy, leaving ripe wheat uncut and livestock untended. Oxen and asses, sheep and goats, pigs and chickens ran wild and they too, according to local reports, succumbed to the pest. English sheep, bearers of the precious wool, died throughout the country. The chronicler Henry Knighton, canon of Leicester Abbey, reported five thousand dead in one field alone, "their bodies so corrupted by the plague that neither beast nor bird would touch them," and spreading an appalling stench. In the Austrian Alps wolves came down to prey upon sheep and then, "as if alarmed by some invisible warning, turned and fled back into the wilderness." In remote Dalmatia bolder wolves descended upon a plague-stricken city and attacked human survivors. For want of herdsmen, cattle strayed from place to place and died in hedgerows and ditches. Dogs and cats fell like the rest.

The dearth of labor held a fearful prospect because the fourteenth century lived close to the annual harvest both for food and for next year's seed. "So few servants and laborers were left," wrote Knighton, "that no one knew where to turn for help." The sense of a vanishing future created a kind of dementia of despair. A Bavarian chronicler of Neuberg on the Danube recorded that "Men and women . . . wandered around as if mad" and let their cattle stray "because no one had any inclination to concern themselves about the future." Fields went uncultivated, spring seed unsown. Second growth with nature's awful energy crept back over cleared land, dikes crumbled, salt water reinvaded and soured the lowlands. With so few hands remaining to restore the work of centuries, people felt, in Walsingham's[6] words, that "the world could never again regain its former prosperity."

Though the death rate was higher among the anonymous poor, the known and the great died too. King Alfonso XI of Castile was the only reigning monarch killed by the pest, but his neighbor King Pedro of Aragon lost his wife, Queen Leonora, his daughter Marie, and a niece in the space of six months. John Cantacuzene, Emperor of Byzantium, lost his son. In France the lame Queen Jeanne and her daughter-in-law Bonne de Luxemburg, wife of the Dauphin, both died in 1349 in the same phase that took the life of Enguerrand's mother. Jeanne, Queen of Navarre, daughter of Louis X, was another victim. Edward III's second daughter, Joanna, who was on her way to marry Pedro, the heir of Castile, died in Bordeaux. Women appear to have been more vulnerable than men, perhaps because, being more housebound, they were more exposed to fleas. Boccaccio's mistress Fiammetta, illegitimate daughter of the King of Naples, died, as did Laura, the beloved—whether real or fictional—of Petrarch. Reaching out to us in the future, Petrarch cried, "Oh happy posterity who will not experience such abysmal woe and will look upon our testimony as a fable."

In Florence Giovanni Villani, the great historian of his time, died at sixty-eight in the midst of an unfinished sentence: ". . . *e dure questo pistolenza fino a* . . . (in the midst of this pestilence there came to an end . . .)." Siena's master painters, the brothers Ambrogio and Pietro

---

[6]Thomas Walsingham (d. ca. 1422), English monk and historian.

Lorenzetti, whose names never appear after 1348, presumably perished in the plague, as did Andrea Pisano, architect and sculptor of Florence. William of Ockham and the English mystic Richard Rolle of Hampole both disappear from mention after 1349. Francisco Datini, merchant of Prato, lost both his parents and two siblings. Curious sweeps of mortality afflicted certain bodies of merchants in London. All eight wardens of the Company of Cutters, all six wardens of the Hatters, and four wardens of the Goldsmiths died before July 1350. Sir John Pulteney, master draper and four times mayor of London, was a victim, likewise Sir John Montgomery, Governor of Calais.

Among the clergy and doctors the mortality was naturally high because of the nature of their professions. Out of twenty-four physicians in Venice, twenty were said to have lost their lives in the plague, although, according to another account, some were believed to have fled or to have shut themselves up in their houses. At Montpellier, site of the leading medieval medical school, the physician Simon de Covino reported that, despite the great number of doctors, "hardly one of them escaped." In Avignon, Guy de Chauliac confessed that he performed his medical visits only because he dared not stay away for fear of infamy, but "I was in continual fear." He claimed to have contracted the disease but to have cured himself by his own treatment; if so, he was one of the few who recovered.

Clerical mortality varied with rank. Although the one-third toll of 25 cardinals reflects the same proportion as the whole, this was probably due to their concentration in Avignon. In England, in strange and almost sinister procession, the Archbishop of Canterbury, John Stratford, died in August 1348, his appointed successor died in May 1349, and the next appointee three months later, all three within a year. Despite such weird vagaries, prelates in general managed to sustain a higher survival rate than the lesser clergy. Among bishops the deaths have been estimated at about one in twenty. The loss of priests, even if many avoided their fearful duty of attending the dying, was about the same as among the population as a whole.

Government officials, whose loss contributed to the general chaos, found, on the whole, no special shelter. In Siena four of the nine members of the governing oligarchy died, in France one third of the royal notaries, in Bristol fifteen out of the fifty-two members of the Town Council or almost one-third. Tax-collecting obviously suffered, with the result that Philip VI was unable to collect more than a fraction of the subsidy granted him by the Estates in the winter of 1347–48.

Lawlessness and debauchery accompanied the plague as they had during the great plague of Athens of 430 B.C., when according to Thucydides, men grew bold in the indulgence of pleasure: "For seeing how the rich died in a moment and those who had nothing immediately inherited their property, they reflected that life and riches were alike transitory and they resolved to enjoy themselves while they could." Human behavior is timeless. When St. John had his vision of plague in Revelation, he knew from some experience or race memory that those who survived "repented not of the work of their hands. . . . Neither repented they of their murders, nor of their sorceries, nor of their fornication, nor of their thefts."

Ignorance of the cause augmented the sense of horror. Of the real carriers, rats and fleas, the fourteenth century had no suspicion, perhaps because they were so familiar. Fleas, though a common household nuisance, are not once mentioned in contemporary plague writings, and rats only incidentally, although folklore commonly associated them with pestilence. The legend of the Pied Piper[7] arose from an outbreak of 1284. The actual plague bacillus, *Pasturella pestis*, remained undiscovered for another five hundred years. Living alternately in the stomach of the flea and the bloodstream of the rat who was the flea's host, the bacillus in its bubonic form was transferred to humans and animals by the bite of either rat or flea. It traveled by virtue of *Rattus rattus*, the small medieval black rat that lived on ships, as well as by the heavier brown or sewer rat. What precipitated the turn of the bacillus from innocuous to virulent form is unknown, but the occurrence is now believed to have taken place not in China but somewhere in central Asia

---

[7]The legend has it that the piper was being paid to lead rats out of the town of Hamelin, Germany, but after he completed his task, the town refused to pay, and the piper, in revenge, led Hamelin's children out of town, never to be seen again.

and to have spread along the caravan routes. Chinese origin[8] was a mistaken notion of the fourteenth century based on real but belated reports of huge death tolls in China from drought, famine, and pestilence which have since been traced to the 1330s, too soon to be responsible for the plague that appeared in India in 1346.

The phantom enemy had no name. Called the Black Death only in later recurrences, it was known during the first epidemic simply as the Pestilence or Great Mortality. Reports from the East, swollen by fearful imaginings, told of strange tempests and "sheets of fire" mingled with huge hailstones that "slew almost all," or a "vast rain of fire" that burned up men, beasts, stones, trees, villages, and cities. In another version, "foul blasts of wind" from the fires carried the infection to Europe "and now as some suspect it cometh round the seacoast." Accurate observation in this case could not make the mental jump to ships and rats because no idea of animal- or insect-borne contagion existed.

The earthquake was blamed for releasing sulfurous and foul fumes   30
from the earth's interior, or as evidence of a titanic struggle of planets and oceans causing waters to rise and vaporize until fish died in masses and corrupted the air. All these explanations had in common a factor of poisoned air, of miasmas and thick, stinking mists traced to every kind of natural or imagined agency from stagnant lakes to malign conjunction of the planets, from the hand of the Evil One to the wrath of God. Medical thinking, trapped in the theory of astral influences, stressed air as the communicator of disease, ignoring sanitation or visible carriers. The existence of two carriers confused the trail, the more so because the flea could live and travel independently of the rat for as long as a month and, if infected by the particularly virulent septicemic form of the bacillus, could infect humans without reinfecting itself

[8]Although the idea of Chinese origin is still being repeated (e.g., by William H. McNeill, *Plagues and People*, New York, 1976, 161–63), it is disputed by L. Carrington Goodrich of the Association for Asian Studies, Columbia Univ., in letters to the author of 18 and 26 October 1973. Citing contemporary Chinese and other sources, he also quotes Dr. George A. Perera of the College of Physicians and Surgeons, an authority or communicable diseases, who "agrees with me that the spaces between epidemics in China (1334), Semirechyé (1338–39) and the Mediterranean basin (1347–49) seem too long for the first to be responsible for the last." [Author's Note.]

from the rat. The simultaneous presence of the pneumonic form of the disease, which was indeed communicated through the air, blurred the problem further.

The mystery of the contagion was "the most terrible of all the terrors," as an anonymous Flemish cleric in Avignon wrote to a correspondent in Bruges. Plagues had been known before, from the plague of Athens (believed to have been typhus) to the prolonged epidemic of the sixth century A.D., to the recurrence of sporadic outbreaks in the twelfth and thirteenth centuries, but they had left no accumulated store of understanding. That the infection came from contact with the sick or with their houses, clothes, or corpses was quickly observed but not comprehended. Gentile da Foligno, renowned physician of Perugia and doctor of medicine at the universities of Bologna and Padua, came close to respiratory infection when he surmised that poisonous material was "communicated by means of air breathed out and in." Having no idea of microscopic carriers, he had to assume that the air was corrupted by planetary influences. Planets, however, could not explain the ongoing contagion. The agonized search for an answer gave rise to such theories as transference by sight. People fell ill, wrote Guy de Chauliac, not only by remaining with the sick but "even by looking at them." Three hundred years later Joshua Barnes, the seventeenth century biographer of Edward III, could write that the power of infection had entered into beams of light and "darted death from the eyes."

Doctors struggling with the evidence could not break away from the terms of astrology, to which they believed all human physiology was subject. Medicine was the one aspect of medieval life, perhaps because of its links with the Arabs, not shaped by Christian doctrine. Clerics detested astrology, but could not dislodge its influence. Guy de Chauliac, physician to three popes in succession, practiced in obedience to the zodiac. While his *Cirurgia* was the major treatise on surgery of its time, while he understood the use of anesthesia made from the juice of opium, mandrake, or hemlock, he nevertheless prescribed bleeding and purgatives by the planets and divided chronic from acute diseases on the basis of one being under the rule of the sun and the other of the moon.

In October 1348 Philip VI asked the medical faculty of the University of Paris for a report on the affliction that seemed to threaten human survival. With careful thesis, antithesis, and proofs, the doctors ascribed it to a triple conjunction of Saturn, Jupiter, and Mars in the fortieth degree of Aquarius said to have occurred on March 20, 1345. They acknowledged, however, effects "whose cause is hidden from even the most highly trained intellects." The verdict of the masters of Paris became the official version. Borrowed, copied by scribes, carried abroad, translated from Latin into various vernaculars, it was everywhere accepted, even by the Arab physicians of Cordova and Granada, as the scientific if not the popular answer. Because of the terrible interest of the subject, the translations of the plague tracts stimulated use of national languages. In that one respect, life came from death.

To the people at large there could be but one explanation—the wrath of God. Planets might satisfy the learned doctors, but God was closer to the average man. A scourge so sweeping and unsparing without any visible cause could only be seen as Divine punishment upon mankind for its sins. It might even be God's terminal disappointment in his creature. Matteo Villani compared the plague to the Flood in ultimate purpose and believed he was recording "the extermination of mankind." Efforts to appease Divine wrath took many forms, as when the city of Rouen ordered that everything that could anger God, such as gambling, cursing, and drinking, must be stopped. More general were the penitent processions authorized at first by the Pope, some lasting as long as three days, some attended by as many as two thousand, which everywhere accompanied the plague and helped to spread it.

Barefoot in sackcloth, sprinkled with ashes, weeping, praying, tearing their hair, carrying candles and relics, sometimes with ropes around their necks or beating themselves with whips, the penitents wound through the streets, imploring the mercy of the Virgin[9] and saints at their shrines. In a vivid illustration for the *Très Riches Heures*[1] of the Duc de Berry, the Pope is shown in a penitent procession attended by four cardinals in scarlet from hat to hem. He raises both

[9]That is, the Virgin Mary, mother of Jesus.
[1]An illustrated, or illuminated, book of prayers.

Très Riches Heures of the Duc de Berry, by Polde Limbourg, c. 1410

arms in supplication to the angel on top of the Castel Sant' Angelo, while white-robed priests bearing banners and relics in golden cases turn to look as one of their number, stricken by the plague, falls to the ground, his face contorted with anxiety. In the rear, a gray-clad monk falls beside another victim already on the ground as the townspeople gaze in horror. (Nominally the illustration represents a sixth-century plague in the time of Pope Gregory the Great, but as medieval artists made no distinction between past and present, the scene is shown as the artist would have seen it in the fourteenth century.) When it became evident that these processions were sources of infection, Clement VI had to prohibit them.

In Messina, where the plague first appeared, the people begged the Archbishop of neighboring Catania to lend them the relics of St. Agatha. When the Catanians refused to let the relics go, the Archbishop dipped them in holy water and took the water himself to Messina, where he carried it in a procession with prayers and litanies through the streets. The demonic, which shared the medieval cosmos with God, appeared as "demons in the shape of dogs" to terrify the people. "A black dog with a drawn sword in his paws appeared among them, gnashing his teeth and rushing upon them and breaking all the silver vessels and lamps and candlesticks on the altars and casting them hither and thither. . . . So the people of Messina, terrified by this prodigious vision, were all strangely overcome by fear."

The apparent absence of earthly cause gave the plague a supernatural and sinister quality. Scandinavians believed that a Pest Maiden emerged from the mouth of the dead in the form of a blue flame and flew through the air to infect the next house. In Lithuania the Maiden was said to wave a red scarf through the door or window to let in the pest. One brave man, according to legend, deliberately waited at his open window with drawn sword and, at the fluttering of the scarf, chopped off the hand. He died of his deed, but his village was spared and the scarf long preserved as a relic in the local church.

Beyond demons and superstition the final hand was God's. The Pope acknowledged it in a Bull of September 1348, speaking of the "pestilence with which God is afflicting the Christian people." To the Emperor John Cantacuzene it was manifest that a malady of such horrors, stenches, and agonies, and especially one bringing the dismal despair that settled upon its victims before they died, was not a plague "natural" to mankind but "a chastisement from Heaven." To Piers Plowman[2] "these pestilences were for pure sin."

The general acceptance of this view created an expanded sense of guilt, for if the plague were punishment there had to be terrible sin to have occasioned it. What sins were on the fourteenth century conscience? Primarily greed, the sin of avarice, followed by usury, worldliness, adultery, blasphemy, falsehood, luxury, irreligion. Giovanni Villani, attempting to account for the cascade of calamity that had fallen upon Florence, concluded that it was retribution for the sins of

---

[2]Main character of an medieval English poem by the same name, written by William Langland (c. 1332–c. 1386).

avarice and usury that oppressed the poor. Pity and anger about the condition of the poor, especially victimization of the peasantry in war, was often expressed by writers of the time and was certainly on the conscience of the century. Beneath it all was the daily condition of medieval life, in which hardly an act or thought, sexual, mercantile, or military, did not contravene the dictates of the Church. Mere failure to fast or attend mass was sin. The result was an underground lake of guilt in the soul that the plague now tapped.

That the mortality was accepted as God's punishment may explain 40 in part the vacuum of comment that followed the Black Death. An investigator has noticed that in the archives of Périgord references to the war are innumerable, to the plague few. Froissart mentions that great death but once, Chaucer[3] gives it barely a glance. Divine anger so great that it contemplated the extermination of man did not bear close examination.

* * *

[3]Geoffrey Chaucer (c. 1343–1400), English author of *The Canterbury Tales.*

STUDY QUESTIONS

1. What is the Black Death? When did it occur and how did it spread? What were its effects on cities, rural areas, and institutions?

2. Tuchman uses CLASSIFICATION AND DIVISION to ORGANIZE her essay. What classifications does she use? How effective do you find this organization? Explain.

3. How would you characterize Tuchman's TONE in this selection? What is the author's attitude toward the doctors, clergy, and others? How does this attitude affect your reading?

4. *For Writing.* Select another epidemic—or a potential epidemic—in history, such as the 1918 influenza pandemic or the recent concerns over a swine flu epidemic. RESEARCH the epidemic and the disease and write an essay in which you explain the causes and symptoms of the disease and ANALYZE the history of the epidemic—how the illness spread (or is likely to spread), how people responded to the epidemic (or are likely to respond), and how it affected (or will affect) society.

WALT WHITMAN $\Bigg\{$ *When I Heard the*
Learn'd Astronomer

WALT WHITMAN (1819–1892), American poet and journalist, was born on a farm on Long Island but moved to Brooklyn with his family when he was four. Beginning his working life with little formal education, Whitman took a job in a newspaper office when he was twelve; by his mid-teens he was writing articles for New York newspapers. After years of work as a journalist and schoolteacher, Whitman began experimenting with poetry. By the early 1850s he had evolved a style all his own and envisioned a vehicle for his poems, a volume he would call *Leaves of Grass*. He self-published the first edition of *Leaves* in 1855 and continued adding to and revising subsequent editions until his death. Although Whitman's free-verse celebration of democratic ideals and open sexuality was radical at the time of its publication, *Leaves of Grass* has become one of the most influential collections of poetry in the American literary canon.

In "When I Heard the Learn'd Astronomer," Whitman contrasts two ways of knowing: the scientific and the experiential. Grounded in the American Romantic tradition, Whitman believed that direct experience led to a more profound understanding of reality, an understanding that transcended what could be known through study and logic. As you read, notice how the form and diction of this eight-line poem help to emphasize the contrast between these two ways of knowing.

When I heard the learn'd astronomer,
When the proofs, the figures, were ranged in columns before me,
When I was shown the charts and diagrams, to add, divide, and measure them,
When I sitting heard the astronomer where he lectured with much applause in the lecture-room,

How soon unaccountable I became tired and sick,   5
Till rising and gliding out I wander'd off by myself,
In the mystical moist night-air, and from time to time,
Look'd up in perfect silence at the stars.

STUDY QUESTIONS

1. Why does the SPEAKER become "tired and sick"? What is his remedy?

2. Whitman's poem can be divided into two parts, each consisting of four lines: the first part takes place in a lecture hall; the second, outside under the night sky. ANALYZE Whitman's word choice in each section. Consider the following:

   • How does the IMAGERY in the first four lines differ from that in the second?

   • What is the effect of repeating the word "When" in the first four lines? Why does Whitman drop this repetition in the last four?

   • What VERBS dominate the first part? The second?

3. While we may not generally think of a poetry as a means of PERSUASION, "When I Heard the Learn'd Astronomer" is clearly making an ARGUMENT. Based on your examination of Whitman's DICTION and imagery, articulate the central CLAIM that he makes in this poem.

4. *For Writing.* Choose another poem or lyric that isn't overtly advancing an argument. After analyzing the poem's form, action, diction, and imagery, write an essay in which you identify an argument the writer is likely making, though perhaps in an oblique way. Consider the effectiveness of this poem or lyric as a means of persuasion, given the writer's AUDIENCE.

E. O. WILSON { *Apocalypse Now*

EDWARD O. WILSON (b. 1929), biologist, naturalist, and writer, was born in Birmingham, Alabama. He earned three degrees in biology: a BS in 1949 and an MS in 1950, both from the University of Alabama, and a PhD in 1955 from Harvard University. He joined Harvard's faculty in 1956, where he remained his entire career. Regarded as one of the most important scientists of the twentieth century, Wilson has discovered hundreds of new insect species and has written extensively on biodiversity and sociobiology, the study of how biology influences the behavior of organisms. Wilson won the National Medal for Science in 1977 and has received two Pulitzer Prizes, for *On Human Nature* (1979) and *The Ants* (1991).

"Apocalypse Now," Wilson's letter to a fictional Southern Baptist minister, originally appeared in *The New Republic*. Acknowledging their different worldviews but highlighting the things they have in common, Wilson asks the minister to join him in working to stop environmental destruction. Without an alliance between science and religion to "save the Creation," Wilson argues, our survival as a species is in jeopardy. As you read, consider how—and how effectively—Wilson establishes common ground with his fictional minister and, more broadly, the evangelical Christian community he hopes to reach.

DEAR PASTOR,

We have not met, yet I feel I know you well enough to call you a friend. First of all, we grew up in the same faith. As a boy, I, too, answered the altar call; I went under the water. Although I no longer belong to that faith, I am confident that, if we met and spoke privately of

"Apocalypse Now" by Edward O. Wilson. Originally published in *The New Republic*, September 4, 2006. Reprinted by permission of the author.

our deepest beliefs, it would be in a spirit of mutual respect and good-will. I know we share many precepts of moral behavior. Perhaps it also matters that we are both Americans and, insofar as it might still affect civility and good manners, we are both Southerners.

I write to you now for your counsel and help. Of course, in doing so, I see no way to avoid the fundamental differences in our worldviews. You are a strict interpreter of Christian Holy Scripture; I am a secular humanist. You believe that each person's soul is immortal, making this planet a waystation to a second, eternal life; I think heaven and hell are what we create for ourselves, on this planet. For you, the belief in God made flesh to save mankind; for me, the belief in Promethean fire seized to set men free.[1] You have found your final truth; I am still searching. You may be wrong; I may be wrong. We both may be partly right.

Do these differences in worldview separate us in all things? They do not. You and I and every other human being strive for the same imper-atives of security, freedom of choice, personal dignity, and a cause to believe in that is larger than ourselves. Let us see, then, if we can meet on the near side of metaphysics in order to deal with the real world we share. You have the power to help solve a great problem about which I care deeply. I hope you have the same concern. I suggest that we set aside our differences in order to save the Creation. The defense of living nature is a universal value. It doesn't rise from, nor does it pro-mote, any religious or ideological dogma. Rather, it serves without discrimination the interests of all humanity. Pastor, we need your help. The Creation—living nature—is in deep trouble.

Scientists estimate that, if habitat-conversion and other destructive human activities continue at their present rates, half the species of plants and animals on earth could be either gone or at least fated for early extinction by the end of the century. The ongoing extinction rate is calculated in the most conservative estimates to be about 100 times above that prevailing before humans appeared on earth, and it is ex-pected to rise to at least 1,000 times greater (or more) in the next few

[1]Wilson refers to Jesus Christ, on the one hand, and Prometheus, the Titan who stole fire and gave it to mankind, on the other.

decades. If this rise continues unabated, the cost to humanity—in wealth, environmental security, and quality of life—will be catastrophic.

Surely we can agree that each species, however inconspicuous and humble it may seem to us at this moment, is a masterpiece of biology and well worth saving. Each species possesses a unique combination of genetic traits that fits it more or less precisely to a particular part of the environment. Prudence alone dictates that we act quickly to prevent the extinction of species and, with it, the pauperization of earth's ecosystems.

With all the troubles that humanity faces, why should we care about the condition of living nature? Homo sapiens is a species confined to an extremely small niche. True, our minds soar out to the edges of the universe and contract inward to subatomic particles—the two extremes encompassing 30 powers of ten in space. In this respect, our intellects are godlike. But, let's face it, our bodies stay trapped inside a proportionately microscopic envelope of physical constraints. Earth provides a self-regulating bubble that sustains us indefinitely without any thought or contrivance of our own. This protective shield is the biosphere, the totality of life, creator of all air, cleanser of all water, manager of all soil—but is itself a fragile membrane that barely clings to the face of the planet. We depend upon its razor-thin health for every moment of our lives. We belong in the biosphere, we were born here as species, we are closely suited to its exacting conditions—and not all conditions, either, but just those in a few of the climatic regimes that exist upon some of the land. Environmental damage can be defined as any change that alters our surroundings in a direction contrary to humanity's inborn physical and emotional needs. We must be careful with the environment upon which our lives ultimately depend.

In destroying the biosphere, we are destroying unimaginably vast sources of scientific information and biological wealth. Opportunity costs, which will be better understood by our descendants than by ourselves, will be staggering. Gone forever will be undiscovered medicines, crops, timber, fibers, soil-restoring vegetation, petroleum substitutes, and other products and amenities. Critics of environmentalism forget, if they ever knew, how the rosy periwinkle of Madagascar provided the alkaloids that cure most cases of Hodgkin's disease and acute childhood leukemia; how a substance from an obscure Norwegian fungus made possible the organ transplant industry; how a chemical from the saliva of leeches yielded a solvent that prevents blood clots during and after surgery; and so on through the pharmacopoeia that has stretched from the herbal medicines of Stone Age shamans to the magic-bullet cures of present-day biomedical science.

These are just a few examples of what could be lost if Homo sapiens pursue our current course of environmental destruction. Earth is a laboratory wherein nature—God, if you prefer, pastor—has laid before us the results of countless experiments. We damage her at our own peril.

You may well ask at this point, *Why me?* Simply because religion and science are the two most powerful forces in the world today and especially in the United States. If religion and science could be united on the common ground of biological conservation, the problem might soon be solved. 10

It may seem far-fetched for a secular scientist to propose an alliance between science and religion. But the fact is that environmental activists cannot succeed without you and your followers as allies. The political process in American democracy, with rare exceptions, does not start at the top and work its way down to the voting masses. It proceeds in the opposite direction. Political leaders are compelled to calculate as precisely as they can what it will take to win the next election. The United States is an intensely religious nation. It is overwhelmingly Judeo-Christian, with a powerful undercurrent of evangelism. We secularists must face reality. The National Association of Evangelicals has 30 million members; the three leading American humanist organizations combined have, at best, a few thousand. Those who, for religious reasons, believe in saving the Creation, have the strength to do so through the political process; acting alone, secular environmentalists do not. An alliance between science and religion, forged in an atmosphere of mutual respect, may be the only way to protect life on earth, including, in the end, our own.

Yes, the gulf separating our worldviews is wide. The Abrahamic religions—Judaism, Christianity, and Islam—believe that the universe was constructed to be relevant to humanity. The discoveries of science, in unintended opposition, have reduced earth to an infinitesimal speck within an immensity of space unrelated to human destiny. The Abrahamic religions envisage a supreme ruler who, while existing outside the material universe, nevertheless oversees an agenda for each and every one of our immortal souls. Science can find no evidence of an agenda other than that fashioned by the complex interaction of genes and environment within parallel evolving cultures. Religious creation stories have a divinely engineered beginning and a divinely ordained ending. According to science, in contrast, humans descended from apish ancestors: our origin was basically no different from that of other animals, played out over geological time through a tortuous route of mutation and environmentally driven natural selection. In addition, all mainstream religious belief, whether fundamentalist or liberal, is predicated upon the assumption that humanity is not alone, and we are here for a life and purpose beyond our earthly existence. Science says that, as far as verifiable evidence tells, we are alone, and what significance we have is therefore of our own making. This is the heart of the agonizing conflict between science and religion that has persisted for the past 500 years.

I do not see how the difference in worldview between these two great productions of human striving can be closed. But, for the purposes of saving the Creation, I am not sure that it needs to be. To make the point in good gospel manner, let me tell the story of a young man, newly trained for the ministry and so fixed in his Christian faith that he referred all questions of morality to readings from the Bible. When he visited the Atlantic rainforest of Brazil, he saw the manifest hand of God, and in his notebook he wrote, "It is not possible to give an adequate idea of the higher feelings of wonder, admiration, and devotion which fill and elevate the mind." That was Charles Darwin in 1832, early into the voyage of the HMS *Beagle*, before he had given any thought to evolution. And here is Darwin, concluding *On the Origin of Species* in 1859, having first abandoned Christian dogma and then, with his newfound intellectual freedom, formulated the theory of evolution by natural selection: "There is grandeur in this view of life, with its several powers, having been originally breathed into a few forms or into one; and that, whilst this planet has gone cycling on according to the fixed law of gravity, from so simple a beginning endless forms most beautiful and most wonderful have been, and are being, evolved." Darwin's reverence for life remained the same as he crossed the seismic divide that separated his religious phase and his scientific one. And so it can be for the divide that, today, separates mainstream religion and scientific humanism. And that separates you and me.

Indeed, despite all that divides science from religion, there is good reason to hope that an alliance on environmental issues is possible. The spiritual reach of evangelical Christianity is nowadays increasingly extended to the environment. While the Old Testament God commands humanity to take dominion over the earth, the decree is not (as one evangelical leader recently affirmed) an excuse to trash the planet. The dominant theme in scripture as interpreted by many evangelicals is instead stewardship. Organizations like the Green Cross and the Evangelical Environmental Network (the latter a coalition of evangelical Christian agencies and institutions) are expanding their magisterium to include conservation—in religious terms, protection of the living Creation.

This evangelical interest in the environment is part of a worldwide trend among religions. In the United States, the umbrella National Religious Partnership for the Environment works with evangelical groups and other prominent organizations, including the U.S. Conference of Catholic Bishops, the National Council of Churches of Christ, and the Coalition on the Environment and Jewish Life. In 2001, the Archbishop of Canterbury urged that "it may not be time to build an Ark like Noah, but it is high time to take better care of God's creation." Three years earlier, Bartholomew I, Patriarch of the Greek Orthodox Church, had gone further: "For humans to cause species to become extinct and to destroy the biological diversity of God's creation . . . these are sins." He and Pope John Paul II later issued a "Common Declaration" that "God has not abandoned the world. It is His will that His Design and our hope for it will be realized through our co-operation in

15

restoring its original harmony. In our own time we are witnessing a growth of an ecological awareness which needs to be encouraged, so that it will lead to practical programs and initiatives." Unfortunately, a corresponding magnitude of engagement has not yet occurred in Islam or the Eastern religions.

Every great religion offers mercy and charity to the poor. The poor of the world, of whom nearly a billion exist in the "poverty trap" of absolute destitution, are concentrated in the developing countries—the home of 80 percent of the world's population and most of Earth's biodiversity. The solution to the problems of both depends on the recognition that each depends on the other. The desperately poor have little chance to improve their lives in a devastated environment. Conversely, natural environments, where most of the Creation hangs on, cannot survive the press of land-hungry people who have nowhere else to go.

To be sure, some leaders of the religious right are reluctant to support biological conservation, an opposition sufficient to create a wedge within the evangelical movement. They may be partly afraid of paganism, by which worship of nature supplants worship of God. More realistically and importantly, opposition rises from the perceived association of environmental activism with the political left. For decades, conservatives have defined environmentalism as a movement bent on strangling the United States with regulations and bureaucratic power. This canard has dogged the U.S. environmental movement and helped keep it off the agenda of the past two presidential campaigns.

Finally, however, opinion may be changing. The mostly evangelical religious right, which, along with big business, has been the decisive source of power in the Republican Party, has begun to move care of the Creation back into the mainstream of conservative discourse. The opportunity exists to make the environment a universal concern and to render it politically nonpartisan.

Still, for all the positive signs, I remain puzzled that so many religious leaders have hesitated to make protection of the Creation an important part of their magisterium. Pastor, help me understand: Do they believe that human-centered ethics and preparation for the afterlife are the only things that matter? Do they believe that the Second Coming is im-

minent and that, therefore, the condition of the planet is of little consequence? These and other similar doctrines are not gospels of hope and
compassion. They are gospels of cruelty and despair.

You and I are both humanists in the broadest sense: Human welfare   20
is at the center of our thought. So forget our disagreements, I say, and
let us meet on common ground. That might not be as difficult as it first
seems. When you think about it, our metaphysical differences have remarkably little effect on the conduct of our separate lives. My guess is
that you and I are about equally ethical, patriotic, and altruistic. We are
products of a civilization that rose from both religion and the science-
based Enlightenment. We would gladly serve on the same jury, fight
the same wars, and sanctify human life with the same intensity. Surely
we also share a love of the Creation—and an understanding that, however the tensions play out between our opposing worldviews, however
science and religion wax and wane in the minds of men, there remains
the earthborn yet transcendental obligation we are both morally bound
to share.

Warmly and respectfully,
Edward O. Wilson

STUDY QUESTIONS

1. What is Wilson's stated PURPOSE for writing "Apocalypse Now"? Why is he writing to a religious leader rather than, for instance, a political leader?

2. How does Wilson establish COMMON GROUND with the minister he addresses and with the evangelical Christian community in general? How effective are his efforts? Explain. Refer to specific passages in your response.

3. Wilson has in mind an AUDIENCE of evangelical Christians. What are some of the ways that he shapes his ARGUMENT to appeal to them? Cite passages from the text to support your RESPONSE. How successful do you think he is? Explain. What changes might he make if he were writing for a different audience?

4. *For Writing.* Pretend that you are the evangelical pastor whom Wilson is addressing and WRITE A LETTER responding to him. On what points do you agree with Wilson? On what points do you disagree? Do you believe science and religion can join hands on this issue? Why or why not? Before you begin drafting your letter, RESEARCH the REASONS that various religious groups have, as Wilson CLAIMS, opposed environmentalism, and address those reasons in your letter.

FRANCINE WEINBERG

RICHARD BULLOCK   { *Glossary*

W. W. NORTON

ABSTRACT A **genre** of writing that summarizes a book, an article, or a paper, usually in 100–200 words. Authors in some academic fields must provide, at the top of a report submitted for publication, an abstract of its content. The abstract may then appear in a journal of abstracts, such as *Psychological Abstracts*. An *informative abstract* summarizes a complete report; a briefer *descriptive abstract* works more as a teaser; a stand-alone *proposal abstract* (also called a **topic proposal**) requests permission to conduct research, write on a topic, or present a report at a scholarly conference. Key Features: **summary** of basic information • objective description • brevity.

ACTION VERB A **verb** that expresses a physical or mental action (*jump, consider*).

ACTIVE VOICE A grammatical construction in which the subject or agent of the action is also its grammatical subject: *The boy hit the baseball. See also* **passive voice.**

AD HOMINEM ARGUMENT A logical fallacy that attacks someone's character rather than addressing the issues.

ADJECTIVE A modifier that describes a **noun** or **pronoun** (*a _challenging_ task, a _cloudless blue_ sky*).

ADVERB A modifier that tells more about a **verb** (*speak _loudly_*), an **adjective** (*_extremely_ loud*), another adverb (*_very_ loudly*), or a whole **clause** (*_Sometimes_ you need to speak loudly*).

ALLEGORY An extended **metaphor**, in which one thing (usually nonrational, abstract, religious) is implicitly spoken of in terms of something concrete. In an allegory, the comparison is expressed in an entire work or large portion of a work.

ANALYSIS A **genre** of writing that methodically examines a topic or text by breaking it into its parts and noting how they work in relation to one another.

ANECDOTES Brief **narratives** used to illustrate a point.

ANNOTATED BIBLIOGRAPHY A **genre** of writing that gives an overview of the published research and scholarship on a topic. Each entry includes complete publication information and a **summary** or an **abstract** for each source. A *descriptive annotation* summarizes the content of a source without commenting on its value; an *evaluative annotation* gives an opinion about the source along with a description of it. Key Features: statement of the scope • complete bibliographic information • relevant commentary • consistent presentation.

APA STYLE A system of documenting sources used in the social sciences. APA stands for the American Psychological Association. *See also* **documentation.**

APPENDIX A section at the end of a written work for supplementary material that would be distracting in the main part of the text.

APPLICATION LETTERS Letters written to apply for jobs or other opportunities. *See also* **résumés.** Key Features: succinct indication of qualifications • reasonable and pleasing **tone** • conventional, businesslike form.

ARGUING A **strategy** that can be used in any kind of writing to support a **claim** with **reasons** and **evidence.**

ARGUMENT, ARGUMENTATIVE ESSAY A **genre** of writing that uses **reasons** and **evidence** to support a **claim** or **position** and, sometimes, to persuade an **audience** to accept that position.

Key Features: clear and arguable **position** • necessary background • good **reasons** • convincing support for each reason • appeal to readers' values • trustworthy **tone** • careful consideration of other positions.

ARTICLE The word *a, an,* or *the,* used to indicate that a **noun** is indefinite (*a, an*) or definite (*the*).

AUDIENCE Those to whom a text is directed—the people who read, listen to, or view the text. Audience is a key part of every text's **rhetorical situation.**

AUTHORITIES People or texts that are cited as support for a writer's **argument.** A structural engineer may be quoted as an authority on bridge construction, for example. *Authority* also refers to a quality conveyed by a writer who is knowledgeable about his or her subject.

BANDWAGON APPEAL A logical **fallacy** that argues for a thought or an action solely because others support it.

BEGGING THE QUESTION A logical **fallacy** that goes in a circle, assuming as a given what the writer is trying to prove.

BILDUNGSROMAN A novel that depicts the growth and development of a **character** and the character's self-understanding.

BLOCK QUOTATION In a written work, long **quotations** are set off indented and without quotation marks. In **MLA style:** set off text more than four typed lines, indented ten spaces (or one inch) from the left margin. In **APA style:** set off quotes of forty or more words, indented five spaces (or half an inch) from the left margin. *See also* **quotation.**

BLOG From *Web log*, a Web site with frequent postings by its authors, links to other sites, and comments posted by readers. Blogs present personal opinion and so should not be considered authoritative sources.

CAUSE AND EFFECT A **strategy** for analyzing why something occurred and/or what its consequences are. Sometimes cause and effect serves as the **organizing** principle for a whole text.

CBE STYLE A system of documenting sources in the sciences. CBE stands for the Council of Biology Editors. *See also* **documentation.**

CHARACTER (1) A fictional person who acts, appears, or is referred to in a work; (2) a combination of a person's qualities, especially moral qualities, so that such terms as "good" and "bad," "strong" and "weak," often apply.

CHARACTERIZATION The artistic presentation of a person in fiction or nonfiction. A term like "a good character" can, then, be ambiguous—it may mean that the character is virtuous or that he or she is well presented by the writer

regardless of his or her characteristics or moral qualities.

CHRONOLOGICAL ORDER A way of organizing text that proceeds from the beginning of an event to the end. Reverse chronological order proceeds in the other direction, from the end to the beginning. *See also* **in medias res.**

CITATION In a text, the act of crediting information from a source. A citation and its corresponding parenthetical **documentation** or footnote or endnote provide minimal information about the source, and complete bibliographic information appears in a list of **works cited** or **references** at the end of the text.

CLAIM A statement that asserts a belief or position. In an **argument**, a claim needs to be stated in a **thesis** or clearly implied, and requires support with **reasons** and **evidence.**

CLASSIFY AND DIVIDE, CLASSIFICATION AND DIVISION A **strategy** that either groups (classifies) numerous individual items by their similarities (for example, classifying cereal, bread, butter, chicken, cheese, ice cream, eggs, and oil as carbohydrates, proteins, and fats) or breaks (divides) one large category into smaller categories (for example, dividing food into carbohydrates, proteins, and fats). Sometimes classification and/or division serves as the **organizing** principle for a whole text.

CLAUSE A group of words that consists of at least a **subject** and a **predicate**; a clause may be either **independent** or **subordinate**.

CLIMAX The point at which the action stops rising and begins falling or reversing.

CLUSTERING A process for generating ideas and text, in which a writer visually connects thoughts by jotting them down and drawing lines between related items.

COHERENCE The quality that allows an **audience** to follow a text's meaning and to *see* the connections among ideas, sentences, and paragraphs. Elements that can help to achieve coherence include the **title**, a clearly stated or implied **thesis**, **topic sentences**, an easy-to-follow **organization** with clear **transitions**, and **parallelism** among comparable ideas.

COLLABORATION The process of working with others.

COMMA SPLICE Two or more **independent clauses** joined by only a comma: *I live free, I love life.*

COMMON GROUND Shared values. Writers build common ground with **audiences** by acknowledging others' **points of view**, seeking areas of compromise, and using language that includes, rather than excludes, those they aim to reach.

COMPARE AND CONTRAST, COMPARISON AND CONTRAST A strategy that highlights the similarities and differences between items. Using the *block method* of comparison and contrast, a writer discusses all the points about one item and then all the same points about the next item; using the *point-by-point method*, a writer discusses one point for both items before going on to discuss the next point for both items, and so on. Sometimes comparison and/or contrast serves as the **organizing** principle for a whole text.

COMPLEMENT A **noun**, noun phrase, **pronoun**, or **adjective** that modifies either the **subject** or the direct **object** of a sentence. A subject complement follows a **linking verb** and tells more about the subject: *She is <u>a good speaker</u>. She is <u>eloquent</u>.* An object complement describes or renames the direct object: *Critics called the movie <u>a masterpiece</u>. We found the movie <u>enjoyable</u>.*

CONFLICT A struggle between opposing forces, such as between two people, between a person and something in nature or society, or even between two drives, impulses, or parts of the self.

CONVINCE, CONVINCING In argument, to present **evidence**, usually in the form of facts and figures, in support of the writer's opinion. Convincing may differ from **persuading** in that convincing is designed to get the reader to agree while persuading is designed to get the reader to act.

COUNTERARGUMENT In argument, an alternative position or objections to the writer's position. The writer of an argument should not only acknowledge counterarguments but also, if at all possible, accept, accommodate, or refute each counterargument.

CREDIBILITY The sense of trustworthiness that a writer conveys through his or her text.

CRITERIA In an evaluation, the standards against which something is judged.

CUBING A process for generating ideas and text in which a writer looks at a topic in six ways—to describe it, to compare it to something else, to associate it with other things or classify it, to analyze it (*see* analysis), to apply it, and to argue for or against it (*see* argument).

DEDUCTION, DEDUCTIVE REASONING In argument, a method of drawing a conclusion in which the writer asserts that a thing is true based on general or universal premises (moving from the general to the specific): *Every virtue is laudable; kindness is a virtue; therefore kindness is laudable.*

DEFINE, DEFINITION A strategy that gets at the meaning of something. Three main kinds of definitions are the *formal definition*, which may iden-

tify the category that something belongs to and tell what distinguishes it from other things in that category: for example, defining a worm as an invertebrate (a category) with a long, rounded body and no appendages (distinguishing features); the *extended definition*, which, as its name suggests is longer: for example, a paragraph explaining where a worm fits in the animal kingdom and what its closest relatives are; and the *stipulative definition*, which gives the writer's particular use of a term: for example, using the term *worm* to refer to a kind of gummy candy. Sometimes definition serves as the organizing principle for a whole text.

DÉNOUEMENT The final part of a plot, in which the action is resolved.

DESCRIBE, DESCRIPTION A strategy that tells how something looks, sounds, smells, feels, or tastes. Effective description creates a clear dominant impression built from specific details. Description can be *objective, subjective*, or both. Sometimes description serves as the organizing principle for a whole text.

DESIGN The way a text is arranged and presented visually. Elements of design include typeface, color, illustration, layout, and white space. One component of a rhetorical situation, design plays an important part in reaching a text's audience and achieving its purpose.

DIALOGUE A strategy of adding people's own words to a text. A writer often uses dialogue to add detail and interest.

DICTION A writer's choice of words, particularly with regard to clarity, correctness, and/or effectiveness in writing.

DISCOVERY DRAFTING A process of drafting something quickly, mostly for the purpose of discovering what one wants to say.

DIVIDE, DIVISION *See* classify and divide.

DOCUMENTATION Publication information about the sources cited in a text. The documentation usually appears in an abbreviated form in parentheses at the point of citation or in an endnote or a footnote. Complete documentation usually appears as a list of works cited or references at the end of the text. Documentation styles vary by discipline. For example, Modern Language Association (MLA) style requires the author's complete first name if it appears in a source, whereas American Psychological Association (APA) and the Council of Biology Editors (CBE) style requires only the initial of the author's first name.

DOCUMENTED ESSAY A genre of writing in which the writer cites information drawn from other sources. Key Features: use of primary and/or secondary sources • analysis or interpretation • documentation.

DOMINANT IMPRESSION The overall effect created through specific details when a writer describes something.

DOMINO THEORY The theory that if one event is allowed to take place, a series of similar events will follow, as when a line of dominoes is placed on end close together, toppling one will cause the entire line to fall.

DRAFTING The process of putting words on paper or screen. Writers often write several drafts, revising each until they achieve their goal or reach a deadline. At that point, they submit a finished final draft.

EDITING The process of fine-tuning a text—examining each word, phrase, sentence, and paragraph—to be sure that the text is correct and precise and says exactly what the writer intends. *See also* proofreading and revising.

EITHER-OR ARGUMENT A logical fallacy that oversimplifies to suggest that only two possible positions exist on a complex issue. The fallacy is also known as a false dilemma.

ETHNOGRAPHY A genre of writing that uses fieldwork—interviewing and observing—to present a picture of a group of people. Key Features: focus on members of a specific group • observation over time in group's natural setting • close analysis of a few members.

Glossary

ETHOS A mode of persuasion that appeals to the character, feelings, moral nature, or guiding beliefs of a person, group, or institution; in writing, ethos can refer to the attempt by the writer or speaker to demonstrate his or her credibility.

EVALUATION A **genre** of writing that makes a judgment about something—a source, poem, film, restaurant, whatever—based on certain **criteria.** Key Features: **description** of the subject • clearly defined criteria • knowledgeable discussion of the subject • balanced and fair assessment.

EVIDENCE The data you present to support your **reasons.** Such data may include statistics, calculations, **examples,** anecdotes, **quotations,** case studies, or anything else that will **convince** your reader that your reasons are compelling. Evidence should be sufficient (enough to show that the reasons have merit) and relevant (appropriate to the argument you're making).

EXAMPLE, EXEMPLIFICATION A strategy that uses examples to clarify or support a point.

EXPLAINING A PROCESS *See* process analysis.

EXPLETIVE A word such as *it* or *there* that stands in for information provided later in the sentence: *It was difficult to drive on the icy road. There is plenty of food in the refrigerator.*

EXPOSITION, EXPOSITORY (1) In literature, the first part of a plot, where background information is established; (2) in composition and rhetoric, a rhetorical **strategy** whose main purpose is to inform the reader about a subject through explanation, interpretation, clarification, or other means.

FABLE A **genre** of writing that employs a typically legendary story with a lesson to be learned by its **audience.** Key Features: animal characters or personified natural forces • an instructive **purpose** • ends with a moral (a short, easily remembered lesson).

FALLACY, LOGICAL Faulty reasoning that can mislead an **audience.** Fallacies include *ad hominem,* bandwagon appeal, begging the question, either-or argument (also called **false dilemma**), false analogy, **faulty causality** (also called *post hoc, ergo propter hoc*), hasty generalization, and slippery slope.

FALLING ACTION the fourth part of action in a classical **plot,** during which the **audience** sees the effects of the conflict.

FALSE ANALOGY A **fallacy** comparing things that do resemble each other but that are not alike in the most important respects.

FALSE DILEMMA *See* either-or argument.

FAULTY CAUSALITY *See* *post hoc, ergo propter hoc.*

FIELD RESEARCH, FIELDWORK The collection of firsthand data through observation, interviews, and questionnaires or surveys.

FLASHBACK In narrative (*see* **narrate**), an interruption of the main story in order to show an incident that occurred at an earlier time.

FORMAL WRITING Writing intended to be evaluated by someone such as an instructor or read by an **audience** expecting academic or businesslike argument and presentation. Formal writing should be carefully **revised, edited,** and **proofread.** *See also* **informal writing.**

FRAGMENT, SENTENCE A group of words that is capitalized and punctuated as a sentence but is not one, either because it lacks a **subject**, a **verb**, or both, or because it begins with a word that makes it a **subordinate clause.**

FRAME STORY A story that surrounds another story, often used as an introductory device or **organizing** principle.

FREEWRITING A process for generating ideas and text by writing continuously for several minutes without pausing to read what has been written.

FUSED SENTENCE Two or more independent clauses with no punctuation between them: *I live free I love life.*

GENERATING IDEAS AND TEXT A set of processes, such as freewriting, clustering, and looping, that helps writers think of **topics, examples, reasons, evidence,** and other parts of a text.

GENRE A classification of text marked by and expected to have certain key features and to follow certain conventions of style and presentation. In the literary world, readers recognize such genres as the short story and novel (which are expected to have **plots**) and the poem (which may not have a plot but has other characteristics, such as rhythm); in academic and workplace settings, readers and writers focus on other genres, which also meet expectations in content, style, and appearance. Genres include **abstracts, annotated bibliographies, application letters, arguments, ethnographies, evaluations, lab reports, literacy narratives, literary analyses, profiles, proposals, reflections, résumés, reports,** and **textual analyses.**

HASTY GENERALIZATION A fallacy that reaches a conclusion based on insufficient or inappropriately qualified evidence.

HOME PAGE The introductory page of a Web site.

HYPERBOLE An over-the-top exaggeration: *I'll bet you a million bucks I'll get an A on my paper.*

IMAGERY Broadly defined, any sensory detail or evocation in a work; more narrowly, the use of figurative language to evoke a feeling, to call to mind an idea, or to describe an object.

IN MEDIAS RES In the middle of things (Latin); a device for introducing a subject in the middle of the action, rather than at the chronological beginning.

INDEFINITE PRONOUN A pronoun, such as *all, anyone, anything, everyone, everything, few, many, some,* and *something,* that functions like a noun but does not refer to or take the place of a specific noun.

INDEPENDENT CLAUSE A clause, containing a subject and a verb, that can stand alone as a sentence: *She sang. The world-famous soprano sang several popular arias.*

INDUCTION, INDUCTIVE REASONING In argument, a method of drawing a conclusion in which the writer asserts that a thing is true by generalizing from a particular observation (moving from the specific to the general): *All the squirrels I have seen are brown; therefore all squirrels are brown.* Note that this particular observation can be proved wrong, since others have observed white and black squirrels.

INFORMAL WRITING Writing not intended to be evaluated—sometimes not even read—by others. Informal writing is produced primarily to explore ideas or to communicate casually with friends and acquaintances. *See also* formal writing.

INQUIRY, WRITING AS A process for investigating a topic by posing questions, searching for multiple answers, and keeping an open mind.

INTERPRETATION The act of making sense of something or explaining what one thinks it means. Interpretation is the goal of writing a literary analysis or textual analysis.

IRONY A situation or statement characterized by a significant difference between what is expected or understood and what actually happens or is meant.

JOURNALISTIC NARRATIVE A genre of writing that prizes accuracy, objectivity, and balance, telling a story in the most impartial and efficient way possible. Key Features: answers the questions *who, what, where, when, why,* and *how,* usually in the first paragraph • simple writing style • most important facts placed first, details filled in later • includes quotations from people involved.

KEYWORD A term that a researcher inputs when searching databases and online search engines for information.

LAB REPORT A genre of writing that covers the process of conducting an experiment in a controlled setting. Key Features: explicit title • abstract • statement of purpose • methods •

results and discussion • **references** • **appendix** • appropriate format.

LAYOUT The way text is arranged on a page or screen—for example, in paragraphs, in lists, on charts, and with headings.

LETTER WRITING A process of generating ideas and text by going through the motions of writing a letter to someone to explain a topic.

LINK On a Web page, a URL, word, or image that, when clicked, opens a different page.

LINKING VERB A verb that expresses a state of being (*appear, be, feel, seem*).

LISTING A process for generating ideas and text by making lists while thinking about a topic, finding relationships among the notes, and arranging the notes as an outline (*see* **outlining**).

LITERACY NARRATIVE A genre of writing that tells about a writer's experience learning to read or write, or about the role of literacy or knowledge in the writer's life. Key Features: well-told story • vivid detail • indication of the narrative's significance.

LITERACY PORTFOLIO An organized collection of materials showing examples of one writer's progress as a reader and/or writer.

LITERARY ANALYSIS A genre of writing that argues for a particular interpretation of a literary text—most often fiction, poetry, or drama. *See also* **analysis** and **textual analysis**. Key Features: arguable **thesis** • careful attention to the language of the text • attention to patterns or themes • clear interpretation • MLA style.

LITERATURE (1) Literary works, including fiction, poetry, drama, and some nonfiction; (2) the body of written work produced in given field.

LOGICAL FALLACY *See* **fallacy, logical**.

LOGOS A mode of persuasion that appeals to logic; that is, an attempt by the writer or speaker to prove a point through logical reasoning. *See also* **deduction** and **induction**.

LOOPING A process for generating ideas and text in which a writer writes about a topic quickly for several minutes and then summarizes the most important or interesting idea in a sentence, which becomes the beginning of another round of writing and summarizing. The process continues until the writer finds an angle for a paper.

MEDIUM (PL. MEDIA) A means for communicating—for example, in print, with speech, or online. Texts consisting of words are said to use *verbal media* (or oral/aural), whereas photographs, films, and sculptures are examples of *visual media* (though some verbal texts include visual images, and some visual texts include words).

MEMOIR A genre of writing that focuses on something significant from the writer's past. Key Features: good story • vivid details • clear significance.

METAPHOR A figure of speech that makes a comparison without using the word *like* or *as*: "*All the world's a stage /And all the men and women merely players*" (William Shakespeare, *As You Like It* 2.7.138–39).

MLA STYLE A system of documenting sources used in the humanities and fine arts. MLA stands for the Modern Language Association. *See also* documentation.

MODAL A helping **verb** such as *can, could, may, might, must, should, will,* or *would* that indicates probability or necessity.

MODIFIER A word, phrase, or clause that describes or specifies something about another word, phrase, or clause (*a long, informative speech; an intellectually demanding presentation; the actors spoke in union*).

NARRATE, NARRATION, NARRATIVE A strategy for presenting information as a story, for telling what happened. It is a pattern most often associated with fiction, but it shows up in all kinds of writing. When used in an essay, a **report**, or another academic **genre**, a narrative must support a point, not merely tell an interesting story for its own sake. It must also present events in some kind of sequence and include only pertinent detail. Sometimes narrative serves as the **organizing** principle for a whole text. *See also* **literacy narrative**.

NARRATOR/SPEAKER The character or person who tells the story.

NOUN A word that refers to a person, place, animal, thing, or idea (*director, Stephen King, forest, Amazon River, tree frog, notebook, democracy*).

OBJECT A word or phrase that follows a **preposition** or receives the action of a **verb**. In the sentence *I handed him the mail that was on the table, him* is the indirect object and *mail* is the direct object of the verb *handed; table* is the object of the preposition *on*.

ORGANIZING Arranging parts of a text so that the text as a whole has **coherence**. The text may use one **strategy** throughout or may combine several strategies to create a suitable organization.

OUTLINING A process for generating ideas and text or for examining a text. An *informal outline* simply lists ideas and then numbers them in the order that they will appear; a *working outline* distinguishes support from main ideas by indenting the former; a *formal outline* is arranged as a series of headings and indented subheadings, each on a separate line, with letters and numerals indicating relative levels of importance.

PARAPHRASING Rewording a text in about the same number of words but without using the word order or sentence structure of the original. A paraphrase is generally used when you want to include the details of a passage but do not need to quote it word for word. Like a **quotation**, a paraphrase requires **documentation**.

PASSIVE VOICE A grammatical construction in which the object of an action becomes the grammatical subject: *The baseball was hit by the boy. See also* **active voice.**

PATHOS A mode of **persuasion** that appeals to the **audience's** emotions.

PERSONAL ESSAY A **genre** of writing that tells about a personal experience. Key Features: well-told story • vivid detail • indication of the narrative's significance.

PERSUADE, PERSUASION, PERSUASIVE In **argument,** to attempt to motivate your reader to behave in a specific way. Persuading may differ from **convincing** in that convincing is designed to get the reader to agree, while persuading is designed to get the reader to act.

PERSUASIVE ESSAY A **genre** of writing in which the writer presents an **argument**

and attempts to **convince** the reader to agree and then **persuade** the reader to act upon its conclusions. Key Features: logical reasoning • necessary background • convincing **evidence.**

PHRASE A group of words that lacks a **subject,** a **verb,** or both.

PLAGIARISM Using another person's words, syntax, or ideas without giving appropriate credit and **documentation.** Plagiarism is a serious breach of ethics.

PLOT/STRUCTURE The arrangement of the action. Traditionally, a plot has five parts: **exposition, rising action, climax, falling action,** and **dénouement.**

POINT OF VIEW A position from which something is considered.

PORTFOLIO A collection of writing selected by a writer to show his or her work, sometimes including a statement assessing the work and explaining what it demonstrates.

POSITION A statement that asserts a belief or **claim.** In an **argument,** a position needs to be stated in a **thesis** or clearly implied, and requires support with **reasons** and **evidence.**

POST HOC, ERGO PROPTER HOC After this, therefore because of this (Latin); also called **faulty causality.** A **fallacy** of assuming that the first of two events causes the second.

PREDICATE In a sentence or clause, the verb and the words that tell more about the verb—its **complements, modifiers,** and **objects.** In the sentence *Mario forcefully stated his opinion,* the predicate is *forcefully stated his opinion.*

PREPOSITION A word or group of words that tells about the relationship of a **noun** or **pronoun** to another part of the sentence. Some common prepositions are *after, at, because of, before, in, on, on top of, under, until, with,* and *without.*

PRIMARY SOURCE A source such as a literary work, historical document, work of art, or performance that a researcher examines firsthand. Primary sources also include experiments and **field research.** In writing about the Revolutionary War, a researcher would likely consider the Declaration of Independence a primary source and a textbook's description of the writing of the document a **secondary source.**

PROCESS In writing, a series of actions that may include **generating ideas and text, drafting, revising, editing,** and **proofreading** a text. *See also* **process analysis.**

PROCESS ANALYSIS A **strategy** for telling how something is done or how to do something. Sometimes an analysis of a process serves as the **organizing** principle for a whole text.

PROFILE A **genre** of writing that presents an engaging portrait of a person, place, or event based on firsthand **field research.** Key Features: interesting subject • necessary background • distinctive angle • firsthand account • engaging details.

PRONOUN A word that takes the place of a **noun** or functions the way a noun does.

PROOFREADING The final **process** in writing, when a writer checks for correct spelling and punctuation as well as for page order, any missing copy, and the consistent use of typefaces and fonts. *See also* **editing, revising,** and **rewriting.**

PROPOSAL A **genre** of writing that argues for a solution to a problem or suggests some action. *See also* **topic proposal.** Key Features: well-defined problem • recommended solution • answers to anticipated questions • call to action • appropriate **tone.**

PURPOSE A writer's goal: for example, to explore, to express oneself, to entertain, to demonstrate learning, to inform, or to persuade. Purpose is one element of the **rhetorical situation.**

QUESTIONING A **process** of **generating ideas and text** about a topic—asking, for example, *what, who, when, where, how,* and *why,* or other questions.

QUOTATION Someone's words repeated exactly as they were spoken or written. Quotation is most effective when the wording is worth repeating or makes a point so well that no rewording will do it justice, or when a writer wants to cite someone's exact words or quote someone whose opinions disagree with others. Quotations need to be acknowledged with **documentation**.

REASON A statement supporting a **claim** or **position**. A reason, in turn, requires its own support.

REFERENCES (APA) The list of sources at the end of a text prepared **APA style**.

REFLECTION A **genre** of writing that presents a writer's thoughtful, personal exploration of a subject. Key Features: topic intriguing to the writer • some kind of structure • specific details • speculative **tone**.

RELATIVE PRONOUN A pronoun such as *that, which, who, whoever, whom,* and *whomever* that connects a **subordinate clause** to a sentence: *The professor who gave the lecture is my adviser.*

REPORTING A **genre** of writing that presents information as objectively as possible to inform readers about a subject. *See also* **lab report, journalistic narrative.** Key Features: tightly focused topic • accurate, well-researched information • various writing strategies • clear **definitions** • appropriate **design**.

RESEARCH The practice of investigating sources, whether written, oral, or visual, to advance knowledge and to provide support for a writer's **claim**. *See also* **documented essay**.

RESPOND, RESPONDING (TO WRITING), RESPONSE A process of writing in which a reader responds to a writer's work by giving his or her thoughts about the writer's title, beginning, clarity of **thesis**, support and **documentation, organization, stance,** treatment of the **audience,** achievement of **purpose,** handling of the **genre,** ending, and other matters.

RÉSUMÉ A **genre** of writing that summarizes someone's academic and employment history, generally written to submit to potential employers. **Design** and word choice depend on whether a résumé is submitted as a print document or in an electronic or scannable form. Key Features: organization that suits goals and experience • succinctness • design that highlights key information (print) or that uses only one typeface (scannable).

REVISE, REVISION The process of making substantive changes, including additions and cuts, to a draft so that it contains all the necessary information in an appropriate organization. During revision, a writer generally moves from whole-text issues to details with the goals of sharpening the focus and strengthening the argument.

REWRITING A process of composing a new draft from another perspective— from a different point of view, audience, stance, genre, medium, sequence, and so on.

RHETORIC The "art, practice, and study of (ethical) human communication" (Andrea Lunsford). Rhetoric can but doesn't necessarily incorporate the art of persuasion; in the field of composition, the term is not typically used in the sense of insincere or inflated language.

RHETORICAL QUESTION A question asked merely for effect with no answer expected: *What were you thinking?*

RHETORICAL SITUATION The context within which writing or other communication takes place, including **purpose, audience, genre, stance,** and **media/ design.**

RISING ACTION The second of the five parts of plot structure, in which events complicate the situation that existed at the beginning of a work, intensifying the conflict or introducing new conflict.

ROGERIAN ARGUMENT A method of argument, introduced by psychologist Carl Rogers, based on finding common ground on all sides of an issue before stating one's own **position.**

SATIRE A **genre** of writing in which the writer holds up human failings to ridicule and censure. Key Features:

irony • sarcasm • **purpose** of improving the reader.

SECONDARY SOURCE An analysis or interpretation of a **primary source.** In writing about the Revolutionary War, a researcher would likely consider the Declaration of Independence a **primary source** and a textbook's description of writing of the document a secondary source.

SETTING The time and place of the action in a piece of writing.

SIGNAL PHRASE A phrase used to attribute **quoted, paraphrased,** or **summarized** material to a source, as in *she said* or *he claimed.*

SIMILE A figure of speech that compares two items using *like* or *as*: "*Still we live meanly, like ants*" (Henry David Thoreau, *Walden*), "*The Wind begun to knead the Grass—/As Women do a Dough—*" (Emily Dickinson).

SLIPPERY SLOPE A **fallacy** that asserts, without **evidence,** that one event will lead to a series of other events that will culminate in a cataclysm.

SPEAKER The person, not necessarily the author, who is the **voice** of a piece of writing.

STANCE A writer's or speaker's attitude toward his or her subject as conveyed through the **tone** and word choice.

STRATEGY A pattern for organizing text to analyze cause and effect, classify and divide, compare and contrast, define, describe, explain a process, narrate, and so on.

STEREOTYPE A characterization based on the conscious or unconscious assumption that a particular aspect—such as gender, age, ethnic or national identity, religion, occupation, and marital status—is predictably accompanied by certain character traits, actions, even values.

STREAM OF CONSCIOUSNESS A method of writing in which the writer conveys the thoughts and feelings of the speaker or a character through a continuous flow of conscious experience; an interior monologue.

STYLE (1) In writing, the arrangement of sentences, phrases, words, and punctuation to achieve a desired effect; (2) the rules of capitalization, punctuation, and so on recommended for the documentation of a source.

SUBJECT A word or word group, usually including at least one noun or pronoun plus its modifiers, that tells who or what a sentence or clause is about. In the sentence *An increasingly frustrated group of commuters waited for the late bus*, the subject is *An increasingly frustrated group of commuters*.

SUBORDINATE CLAUSE A clause, containing a subject and a verb, that contains a subordinating word and therefore cannot stand alone as a sentence: *He wheezes <u>when he exercises</u>. My roommate, <u>who was a physics major</u>, tutors high school students in science.*

SUMMARY A condensation of a text into a briefer but still faithful version in lieu of a paraphrase or a quotation.

SUMMARY-RESPONSE A genre of writing in which the writer or speaker presents both a summary of a text or texts and responds to the text. Key Features: brief summary of the text • highlights of major points of the text • evaluation of the text.

SYMBOL A person, place, thing, event, or pattern in a literary work that designates itself and at the same time figuratively represents or "stands for" something else. Often the thing or idea represented is more abstract or general; the symbol, more concrete and particular.

SYNTHESIZING IDEAS A way of generating new information or supporting a new perspective by bringing together ideas and information from two or more sources.

TEXTUAL ANALYSIS A genre of writing in which a writer looks at what a text says and how it says it. *See also* analysis and literary analysis. Key Features:

summary of the text • attention to context • clear interpretation • reasonable support for your conclusions.

THEME (1) The central or dominant idea or concern of a work; (2) the statement a poem makes about its subject.

THESIS A claim or statement of a writer's position or main point.

TONE A writer's or speaker's attitude toward his or her readers and subject. A writer's tone reflects his or her stance and may be formal or informal, optimistic or pessimistic, playful, ironic, and so on.

TOPIC The subject of a piece of writing; what a text is about.

TOPIC PROPOSAL A statement of intent to examine a topic; also called a proposal abstract. Some instructors require a topic proposal in order to assess the feasibility of the writing project that a student has in mind. Key Features: concise discussion of the subject • clear statement of the intended focus • rationale for choosing the subject • mention of resources.

TOPIC SENTENCE A sentence, usually the first in a paragraph, that encapsulates what that paragraph is about. The topic sentence often includes a claim that will be supported in the paragraph.

TOULMIN ARGUMENT A six-part method of analyzing the structure of arguments formulated by British philosopher Stephen Toulmin. The elements of this model include the claim, the grounds, the warrant, the backing, the qualifier, and the rebuttal.

TRANSITIONS Words or phrases used to make clear the connection between ideas and text.

VANTAGE POINT The position or standpoint from which a writer describes something.

VERB A word or a group of words that conveys an action (*dance, determine, observe*) or a state of being (*be, seem*) and is an essential element of a sentence or clause.

VOICE The acknowledged or unacknowledged source of a piece of writing's words; the speaker; the "person" telling the story.

WORKS-CITED LIST (MLA) At the end of a researched text prepared MLA style, the list of all the sources cited in the text, with full bibliographic information.